P9-DCI-094

JEPPESEN®

GUIDED FLIGHT DISCOVERY

FLIGHT
INSTRUCTOR
SYLLABUS

Jeppesen

Published in the United States of America
Jeppesen
55 Inverness Drive East, Englewood, CO 80112
www.jeppesen.com

All rights reserved. No part of this publication may be reproduced, stored in a retrieval system, or transmitted in any form or by any means, electronic, mechanical, photocopying, recording or otherwise, without the prior permission of the publisher.

ISBN-13: 978-0-88487-467-6
ISBN-10: 0-88487-467-2

Jeppesen
55 Inverness Dr. East
Englewood, CO 80112-5498
Web Site: www.jeppesen.com
Email: Captain@jeppesen.com
© Jeppesen
All Rights Reserved. Published 2000, 2002, 2003, 2006, 2007
JS344526-004   Printed in the United States of America

FLIGHT INSTRUCTOR COURSES

The *Flight Instructor Syllabus* is designed to meet or exceed the requirements of Title 14 of the Code of Federal Regulations (14 CFR) Part 141, for a flight instructor certification course and additional flight instructor rating courses. An applicant may enroll in the three instructor courses consecutively and become a fully qualified CFI with instrument and multi-engine airplane instructor privileges at the conclusion of the training programs. An applicant who has already acquired a basic flight instructor certificate may add either or both of the additional instructor ratings. The Basic and Instrument Instructor Courses utilize single-engine land airplanes, while the Multi-Engine Instructor Course utilizes multi-engine land airplanes with wing-mounted engines.

_____ *is enrolled in the:*

(Name)

☐ # FLIGHT INSTRUCTOR CERTIFICATION COURSE

For the Flight Instructor Certification Course, the applicant must hold a commercial pilot or ATP certificate with an instrument rating appropriate to the aircraft category and class rating for which the course applies. In addition, the applicant must complete all of the ground training and flight training lessons in Stages I and II.

☐ # FLIGHT INSTRUCTOR INSTRUMENT CERTIFICATION COURSE

For the Flight Instructor Instrument Certification Course, the applicant must hold a valid flight instructor certificate with an airplane category rating and a single-engine land class rating and must complete all of the ground training and flight training lessons in Stages III and IV.

☐ # MULTI-ENGINE FLIGHT INSTRUCTOR RATING COURSE

For the Multi-Engine Flight Instructor Course, the applicant must hold a valid flight instructor certificate with an airplane category rating and a single-engine land class rating and must complete all of the ground training and flight training lessons in Stages V and VI. In addition, the applicant must have at least 15 hours of pilot-in-command experience in multi-engine land airplanes at the completion of the course.

SYLLABUS
TABLE OF CONTENTS

 # PREFACE

INTRODUCTION

The Flight Instructor Courses are coordinated ground and flight training programs. They follow a careful, step-by-step progression of subject introduction and practice, incorporating academic assignments and the training aircraft. The structure of the syllabus is not overly complex, but it does require a thorough understanding on the part of the instructor if maximum benefit is to be obtained. When the principles and general order of the syllabus are put into practice, they make the difference between an effective program and a succession of lessons that lack order and direction. The lesson plan outlines should be considered guides to the instructional process. They provide a high degree of flexibility for adapting to individual instructor applicant needs.

COURSE ELEMENTS

As indicated in the Preface, the Flight Instructor Courses are based on the current Part 141 requirements. The Basic and Multi-Engine Course requirements are outlined in Part 141, Appendix F, and the Flight Instructor Instrument Certification Course is outlined in Part 141, Appendix G. In addition to regulatory compliance, the courses contain the areas of operation, tasks, and terminology published in the *Flight Instructor Practical Test Standards (PTS)*. Instructors and student instructor applicants should be familiar with both the applicable regulations and PTS criteria.

GROUND TRAINING

In accordance with Part 141, ground training is an integral part of pilot certification courses. The ground training section of the syllabus meets this requirement. It may be coordinated with the flight training section or used as a separate ground training course.

If the ground training section is coordinated with the flight training section, each ground lesson is conducted at the point indicated in the flight syllabus. This is the most effective method for course utilization because the academic knowledge is essential for application during flight training.

When the course is presented as a formal classroom program, lessons should be followed as outlined in the ground syllabus. However, to provide a degree of flexibility for adapting to individual student needs and the training situation, the syllabus lessons may be altered with approval of the chief flight instructor. Any deviation should not disturb the course continuity or objective. Each lesson may be presented in one classroom session, or it may be divided into two or more sessions, as necessary.

USING THE GROUND LESSONS

The ground lessons generally are divided into three sections: lesson introduction, video presentation, and class discussion. During the lesson introduction, the instructor should outline the subject material to be covered during the training session, the objective for learning that information, and the performance standards necessary for successful lesson completion.

TEXTBOOKS

Prior to the selected ground lesson, the applicant should read and study the assigned textbook section or chapter. The *Flight Instructor* textbook is comprehensive and well illustrated. It contains the essential information necessary to complete the academic stages of the flight instructor courses. Flight instructor instrument applicant also should review selected chapters of the *Instrument/Commercial* textbook as indicated in Stage III and IV Ground Training Lessons.

DVD PRESENTATIONS

Selected lessons include video presentations from the Flight Instructor Video Course which are viewed after the lesson introduction. These presentations include subjects specifically designed for the Flight Instructor Course as well as

selected subjects from the Private, Instrument, and Commercial Video Courses. Also included are videos from Jeppesen's CFI Renewal Program. Schools that have access to Private, Instrument, Commercial, and Multi-Engine Video Courses may assign additional videos to complement appropriate ground lessons. These additional video presentations can be credited toward meeting the ground training time requirements.

During the video presentations, the applicant should feel free to ask questions and obtain clarification of subject material, as necessary. After the applicant has viewed the audiovisual material, the instructor conducts a discussion session. The purpose of the discussion is to elaborate on the subject material and answer any questions the applicant may have.

EXERCISES AND STAGE EXAMS

The final step is for the applicant to complete the appropriate questions at the end of each section in the *Flight Instructor* textbook and discuss any incorrect responses with the instructor. This ensures understanding of the subject material prior to beginning the next ground lesson. When the lesson is complete, the instructor assigns the new material for out-of-class reading. At the end of each stage, the applicant must successfully complete the assigned stage exam. For example, at the end of Stage I, the applicant is required to complete the Basic Flight Instructor Stage I Exam as outlined in the syllabus prior to moving to Stage II.

END-OF-COURSE EXAMS

When all of the appropriate ground lesson assignments are complete, the applicant should take the appropriate Flight Instructor Final Exams. Following the exams, the instructor should conduct a thorough critique of the exam results. In addition, the instructor should assign appropriate subject areas for review.

PILOT BRIEFINGS

The Pilot Briefings are found in Section C of the Flight Instructor Courses Instructors Guide Insert. Each briefing consists of a series of questions which provide comprehensive coverage of selected areas of instruction. The applicant should complete the appropriate briefing in advance of the actual tutoring session. In this way, the applicant will have the opportunity to prepare properly by researching the answers and, therefore, gain optimum benefit from the session. The briefings should be conducted as private tutoring sessions to test each applicant's comprehension. Every question should be discussed thoroughly to ensure the applicant understands the relevant aspects of the question.

PRACTICE GROUND INSTRUCTION

Four practice ground instruction sessions (5 hours total) are included in the Basic Flight Instructor Certification Course. These sessions allow the applicant to practice ground instruction techniques and to perfect methods of organization and delivery. Prior to each of these practice lessons, the instructor will assign the subject area to be presented and the applicant will research the subject and prepare a lesson plan.

The delivery of the planned lesson should be conducted as though the applicant were actually teaching an individual or class. This method of practice helps the applicant learn to communicate clearly and concisely. In addition, these practice sessions also help the applicant prepare for the FAA practical test.

FLIGHT TRAINING

The syllabus provides a standardized course of instruction for a commercial pilot with an instrument rating (airplane) who desires a flight instructor certificate or additional instructor ratings. The syllabus is divided into six stages of training. The basic instructor course is in Stages I and II. The instrument instructor course is in Stages III and IV, and the multi-engine course is in Stages V and VI.

To provide a degree of flexibility for adapting to individual student needs and the training situation, the syllabus flight lessons may be altered with approval of the chief flight instructor. Any deviation should not disturb the course continuity or objective. Each flight lesson may be accomplished during one flight, or it may be divided into two or more flights, as necessary.

HUMAN FACTORS TRAINING

Human factors and aeronautical decision making (ADM) concepts, such as pilot-in-command responsibility, communication, resource use, workload management, and situational awareness should be incorporated into each flight lesson. The lesson objectives contain examples of the ADM principles which apply to the maneuvers and procedures contained in that lesson. As training progresses, the applicant will learn how to teach these principles in conjunction with each lesson and how to evaluate student decision making and judgment skills during flight training.

BASIC INSTRUCTOR

STAGE I

The first stage of training introduces the applicant to the right seat of the training airplane where proficiency in the maneuvers required for private and commercial pilot certification will be acquired. As this stage of training progresses, the applicant will begin to analyze the performance of these maneuvers and make suggestions for improved performance. Near the end of this stage, the applicant will receive instructor training on the operation of a complex airplane from the right seat. In addition, the applicant will increase proficiency in the performance of flight maneuvers from the right seat of the complex airplane.

STAGE II

The flight instructor-airplane applicant will continue to develop the ability to analyze the performance of private and commercial flight maneuvers and offer suggestions for improvement. The sequence of maneuvers to be analyzed follows the normal course of training for the student pilot or commercial pilot applicant beginning with the preflight inspection, progressing through the required maneuvers, and into complex airplane familiarization. The applicant also will learn to teach VFR navigation and administer night checkouts. The stage ends with preparation for the FAA practical test.

INSTRUMENT INSTRUCTOR

STAGE III

This stage introduces the instrument flight instructor applicant to attitude instrument flying from the right seat of the training airplane. As the stage progresses, the applicant will learn basic navigation with both full and partial panel. Holding patterns are next in the training sequence, followed by instrument approach procedures. Near the end of this stage of training the applicant will begin to analyze the performance of maneuvers required for an instrument rating.

STAGE IV

Stage IV continues the instrument flight instructor applicant's education in the techniques of teaching IFR navigation, holding patterns, simulated equipment malfunctions, and full and partial panel instrument maneuvers. IFR approach procedures also are practiced and analyzed during this stage. By the end of the stage, the applicant will be prepared to successfully complete the FAA practical test.

Multi-Engine Instructor

Stage V

During Stage V, the multi-engine flight instructor applicant becomes familiar with the training airplane by practicing the maneuvers required for the multi-engine class rating. The stage progresses with engine-out procedures and maneuvers being demonstrated from the right seat. The applicant completes this stage by providing analysis of the basic multi-engine flight maneuvers.

Stage VI

Stage VI builds on the principles learned in the completion of the previous stage of training. Multi-engine and engine-out operations are taught and analyzed by the multi-engine instructor applicant. Important items are emergency procedures, operations with an engine inoperative including loss of directional control demonstrations, and the use of best engine-out airspeeds. At the conclusion of the stage, the applicant will demonstrate competency in multi-engine airplane instruction and be prepared to successfully complete the FAA practical test.

Preflight Orientation

Prior to each flight, the instructor should provide the applicant with an overview of the subject matter to be covered during the lesson. The instructor should select a quiet, private place to brief the applicant and explain the lesson matter. It is important that the instructor defines unfamiliar terms and explains the maneuvers and objectives of each lesson, since proper preparation of the applicant ensures progress during the lesson.

Airplane Practice

Instruction must be conducted so the applicant obtains the maximum benefit from each flight. This is particularly important in a flight instructor training program which is of relatively short duration, but generally is more expensive per unit of training. Thorough preparation on the part of the instructor and applicant will enhance the productivity of each training session and help to maintain an economical training program.

Postflight Evaluation

The postflight evaluation is equally as important as the preflight orientation. During each postflight session, the applicant should be debriefed thoroughly. Noticeable advancement should be apparent and recommendations should be made for improvement, where appropriate. This action is a valuable instructional technique, because it increases the applicant's retention and, to some degree, prepares for the next lesson.

The instructor must bear in mind that all of the times listed in the Lesson Time Allocation tables are recommended minimums. The time designated in each lesson reflects the time spent with the well-prepared applicant. If necessary, additional time should be allotted.

Stage and End-of-Course Checks

The stage checks in the training syllabus are designed to determine areas of deficiencies and to check the applicant's overall progress in accordance with Part 141. The conduct of stage checks and end-of-course checks is the responsibility of the chief instructor.

However, the chief instructor may delegate the authority to conduct stage checks and end-of-course checks to the assistant chief instructor or a designated check instructor.

TRAINING CREDIT

In accordance with Part 141, Appendix F, the Basic Flight Instructor Certification Course includes 25 hours of flight training and 40 hours of ground training. The Flight Instructor Instrument Certification Course contains 15 hours of flight training and 15 hours of ground training. The Multi-Engine Flight Instructor Rating Course includes 25 hours of flight training and 20 hours of ground training.

Credit for previous training may be applied to the Flight Instructor Certification Course. If the applicant has completed at least two years of study covering the principles of education, in a college or university, 20 hours of credit may be granted toward the required 40 hours of ground training.

If the applicant cannot receive credit for previous training or experience, the entire flight instructor certification course must be completed.

COURSE IMPLEMENTATION

The training syllabus is designed to meet or exceed the requirements of FAR Part 141, Appendix F and Appendix G, which pertain to flight instructor courses. The Instructor's Guide describes the procedures required for obtaining FAA approval under Part 141.

PART 141 OPERATION

The syllabus is presented in both an overview and a lesson-by-lesson format. Lesson sequence and content have been designed to provide the student with maximum academic and flight training prior to the introduction of new maneuvers or procedures. Therefore, the sequence shown in the syllabus outline should not be altered significantly if the coordinated ground and flight training program is utilized.

If the coordinated program is not used, the applicant may complete the ground training and flight training courses separately. When the separate courses are taken, the instructor must be sure the applicant's flight training does not progress faster than the ground training.

PART 61 OPERATION

Although the *Flight Instructor Syllabus* is designed to meet Part 141 requirements, it can be used to meet the knowledge and proficiency requirements of Part 61. Part 61 does not specify a minimum number of hours of flight or ground instruction for the flight instructor training. However, the hours specified in Part 141, Appendix F, or G, must be followed in Part 141 operations. This is not true when the syllabus is used for training under Part 61. In the latter case, the applicant's knowledge and proficiency level determines the number of hours required for flight and ground training.

FLIGHT INSTRUCTOR SYLLABUS

INTRODUCTION

The *Flight Instructor Syllabus* is designed to coordinate the academic study assignments and flight training required by applicants for flight instructor certificates and/or additional ratings. New subject matter is introduced during the ground lessons, which include five items:

1. In-depth textbook assignments
2. DVD presentations
3. Thorough instructor/student discussions
4. Comprehensive review questions
5. Stage and end-of-course exams for evaluation and reinforcement

Optimum effectiveness is realized when ground lessons are completed just prior to the respective flight lessons, as outlined in the syllabus. However, it is also acceptable to present lessons in a formal ground school before the flight instructor applicant is introduced to the airplane. If a considerable length of time has elapsed between the ground lesson and the associated flight, the instructor may wish to conduct a short review of essential material. Flight lessons should not be conducted until related ground lessons have been completed.

FLIGHT INSTRUCTOR CERTIFICATION COURSE

COURSE OBJECTIVES

The applicant will obtain the knowledge, skill, and aeronautical experience necessary to meet the requirements of a flight instructor certificate with an airplane category rating and a single-engine class rating.

COURSE COMPLETION STANDARDS

The applicant will demonstrate through written tests and flight tests, and show through appropriate records, that the knowledge, skill, and experience requirements necessary for a flight instructor certificate with an airplane category rating and a single-engine class rating have been obtained.

GROUND TRAINING COURSE OBJECTIVES

The applicant will obtain the necessary aeronautical knowledge, instructional background, and meet the prerequisites specified in Part 61 for the FAA flight instructor airmen knowledge test.

COMPLETION STANDARDS

The applicant will demonstrate, through oral and written tests and records, that the prerequisites specified in Part 61 have been met and the necessary knowledge to pass the FAA fundamentals of instruction and flight instructor, airplane airmen knowledge tests has been obtained.

FLIGHT TRAINING COURSE OBJECTIVES

The applicant will obtain the aeronautical skill, instructional knowledge, and experience necessary to meet the requirements of a flight instructor certificate with an airplane category rating and a single-engine class rating.

COMPLETION STANDARDS

The applicant will demonstrate, through flight tests and school records, that the aeronautical skill, instructional knowledge, and experience necessary for a flight instructor certificate with an airplane category rating and a single-engine class rating has been obtained.

FLIGHT INSTRUCTOR CERTIFICATION COURSE OVERVIEW

The following time analysis indicates compliance with Part 141, Appendix F.

MINIMUM COURSE HOURS

	GROUND TRAINING					FLIGHT TRAINING			
	Briefing Sessions	AV and Class Discussion	Practice Ground Instruction	Stage / End-of-Course Exams	Exam Debriefings	Maneuver Analysis	Practice Instruction	Stage/ End-of-Course Checks	Preflight/ Postflight Briefings
Stage I		14.0		.5	As Req.	12.0		1.5	As Req.
Stage II	3.5	10.0	5.0	6.0	1.0		13.0	3.5	As Req.
TOTAL	3.5	24.0	5.0	6.5	1.0	12.0	13.0	5.0	As Req.

Note: *The times for stage and end-of-course checks are included in the totals for maneuver analysis and practice instruction.*

APPLICANT INFORMATION

COURSE ENROLLMENT
To enroll in the flight instructor certification course, you must hold a commercial pilot certificate or airline transport pilot certificate with an aircraft category, class, and instrument rating appropriate to the flight instructor category and class rating for which the course applies.

REQUIREMENTS FOR GRADUATION
To obtain a flight instructor certificate you must be at least 18 years of age and be able to read, write, understand, and converse fluently in English. In addition, you must successfully complete all of the ground and flight training lessons contained in Stages I and II.

LESSON DESCRIPTION AND STAGES OF TRAINING
Each lesson is fully described within the syllabus, including the objectives, standards, and measurable units of accomplishment and learning for each lesson. The objectives and standards of each stage are described within the syllabus.

TESTS AND CHECKS
The syllabus incorporates stage checks in accordance with Part 141. These checks are given by the chief instructor, the designated assistant, or check instructor at the end of each stage. You also will complete the appropriate stage exams, pilot briefings, and final examinations that are described within the syllabus. In addition, you must satisfactorily accomplish an end-of-course test after all of the stages have been completed.

LESSON TIME ALLOCATION

Ground Training						Flight Training		
Pilot Briefings	AV Presentation & Class Discussion	Practice Ground Instruction	Stage & End-of-Course Exam Completion	Stage & End-of-Course Exam Debriefing		Maneuver Analysis	Practice Instruction	Stage/E-O-C Checks
					STAGE I			
1.5					Ground Lesson 1			
					Flight Lesson 1	1.5		
1.0					Ground Lesson 2			
1.0					Ground Lesson 3			
					Flight Lesson 2	1.0		
1.5					Ground Lesson 4			
					Flight Lesson 3	1.5		
1.0					Ground Lesson 5			
1.0					Ground Lesson 6			
					Flight Lesson 4	2.5		
1.0					Ground Lesson 7			
					Flight Lesson 5	1.0		
1.0					Ground Lesson 8			
1.0					Ground Lesson 9			
					Flight Lesson 6	1.5		
1.0					Ground Lesson 10			
1.0					Ground Lesson 11			
1.0					Ground Lesson 12			
					Flight Lesson 7	1.5		
1.0					Ground Lesson 13			
		.5	As Req.		Ground Lesson 14 – Stage I Exam			
					Flight Lesson 8 – Stage Check	1.5		1.5
14.0		.5	As Req.		**Stage Totals**	12.0		1.5

NOTE: *Individual times shown are for guidance only; they are not mandatory for each lesson. However, the totals in each category should be attained at the completion of each stage to ensure the student will acquire the minimum instruction required by Part 141. Preflight and postflight briefing times are as required.*

LESSON TIME ALLOCATION

Ground Training						Flight Training		
Pilot Briefings	AV Presentation & Class Discussion	Practice Ground Instruction	Stage & End-of-Course Exam Completion	Stage & End-of-Course Exam Debriefing		Maneuver Analysis	Practice Instruction	Stage/E-O-C Checks
					STAGE II			
	2.0				Ground Lesson 15			
	2.0				Ground Lesson 16			
					Flight Lesson 9		1.5	
	2.0				Ground Lesson 17			
					Flight Lesson 10		1.5	
		1.0			Ground Lesson 18			
					Flight Lesson 11		1.0	
		1.0			Ground Lesson 19			
					Flight Lesson 12		1.5	
	2.0				Ground Lesson 20			
	2.0				Ground Lesson 21			
					Flight Lesson 13		1.0	
		1.5			Ground Lesson 22			
		1.5			Ground Lesson 23			
					Flight Lesson 14		1.5	
2.0					Ground Lesson 24 – FOI Briefing			
1.5			.5		Ground Lesson 25 – Oral Briefing and Stage II Exam			
					Flight Lesson 15		1.5	
			2.5	.5	Ground Lesson 26 – Final Exam – FOI			
			3.0	.5	Ground Lesson 27 – End-of-Course Exam			
					Flight Lesson 16 – Stage Check		1.5	1.5
					Flight Lesson 17 – End-of-Course Check		2.0	2.0
3.5	10.0	5.0	6.0	1.0	**Stage Totals**		13.0	3.5
3.5	24.0	5.0	6.5	1.0	**Course Totals**	12.0	13.0	5.0

NOTE: *Individual times shown are for guidance only; they are not mandatory for each lesson. However, the totals in each category should be attained at the completion of each stage to ensure the student will acquire the minimum instruction required by Part 141. Preflight and postflight briefing times are as required.*

FLIGHT INSTRUCTOR GROUND TRAINING SYLLABUS

STAGE I

STAGE OBJECTIVES

During Stage I, the applicant will become familiar with learning theories, styles and domains of learning, and communication techniques. The applicant will learn about the teaching process, teaching methods, lesson plans, evaluation of student performance, and human factors.

STAGE COMPLETION STANDARDS

This stage is complete when the applicant has completed the Basic Flight Instructor Stage I Exam with a minimum passing score of 80 percent and the instructor has reviewed each incorrect response with the applicant to ensure complete understanding.

STAGE I

GROUND LESSON 1

LESSON REFERENCES:

FLIGHT INSTRUCTOR TEXTBOOK
Chapter 1, Foundations of Learning, Section A — Discovering Learning Theories, and Section B — Exploring Learning Styles and Domains

GFD FLIGHT INSTRUCTOR VIDEO
Vol I — The Flight Instructor and Foundations of Learning

RECOMMENDED SEQUENCE:
NOTE: *Students should read Chapter 1, Sections A and B, prior to Ground Lesson 1.*

1. Lesson Introduction and Video Presentation
2. Class Discussion

LESSON OBJECTIVES:
During this lesson, the applicant will be introduced to learning theories, including the principles of the learning process and how they are applied to flight training. The applicant will understand how each of the elements of the learning process are interrelated. In addition, the applicant will become familiar with the characteristics of learning, learning styles, domains of learning, and the transfer of learning.

CONTENT:

SECTION A — DISCOVERING LEARNING THEORIES
❏ Learning Defined
❏ Behaviorism

- ❑ Cognitive Theory
- ❑ Constructivism
- ❑ Perception and Insights
- ❑ Forgetting and Retention
- ❑ Characteristics of Learning
- ❑ Principles of Learning

SECTION B — EXPLORING LEARNING STYLES AND DOMAINS

- ❑ Learning Styles
- ❑ Domains of Learning
- ❑ Cognitive Domain
- ❑ Psychomotor Domain
- ❑ Affective Domain
- ❑ Transfer of Learning

COMPLETION STANDARDS:

The applicant will complete Chapter 1A and 1B questions with a minimum passing score of 80 percent, and the instructor will review each incorrect response to ensure complete understanding before progressing to Ground Lesson 2.

STUDY ASSIGNMENT:

FLIGHT INSTRUCTOR TEXTBOOK

Chapter 1, Section C — Exchanging Ideas

STAGE I

GROUND LESSON 2

LESSON REFERENCES:

RECOMMENDED SEQUENCE:

FLIGHT INSTRUCTOR TEXTBOOK

Chapter 1, Section C — Exchanging Ideas

1. Lesson Introduction
2. Class Discussion

LESSON OBJECTIVES:

During this lesson, the applicant will learn the basic principles of effective communication. In addition, the applicant will learn the barriers to communication and how to avoid them during instruction.

CONTENT:

SECTION C — EXCHANGING IDEAS

- ❑ Communication Process
- ❑ Source
- ❑ Symbols
- ❑ Receiver
- ❑ Barriers to Effective Communication
- ❑ Lack of Common Experience
- ❑ Confusion Between the Symbol and Symbolized Object
- ❑ Overuse of Abstractions
- ❑ Interference
- ❑ Developing Communication Skills
- ❑ Instructional Communication
- ❑ Practicing Communication
- ❑ Effective Listening

COMPLETION STANDARDS:
The applicant will complete Exercise 1C with a minimum passing score of 80 percent, and the instructor will review each incorrect response to ensure complete understanding before the applicant progresses to Ground Lesson 3.

STUDY ASSIGNMENT:

FLIGHT INSTRUCTOR TEXTBOOK

Chapter 2, Section A — Introducing the Teaching Process

STAGE I

GROUND LESSON 3

LESSON REFERENCES:

FLIGHT INSTRUCTOR TEXTBOOK

Chapter 2 — The Art and Science of Teaching, Section A — Introducing the Teaching Process

GFD FLIGHT INSTRUCTOR VIDEO

Vol I — The Art and Science of Teaching

RECOMMENDED SEQUENCE:
1. Lesson Introduction and Video Presentation
2. Class Discussion

LESSON OBJECTIVES:
During this lesson, the applicant will learn the principles of the teaching process used in the classroom or for individual instruction. Specifically, the applicant will learn how to apply the four basic steps normally required for effective teaching.

CONTENT:

SECTION A — INTRODUCING THE TEACHING PROCESS
☐ Preparation
☐ Performance-Based Objectives
☐ Description of the Skill or Behavior
☐ Conditions
☐ Criteria
☐ Other Uses of Performance-Based Objectives
☐ Presentation
☐ Application
☐ Review and Evaluation

COMPLETION STANDARDS:
The applicant will complete Chapter 2A questions with a minimum passing score of 80 percent, and the instructor will review each incorrect response to ensure complete understanding before the applicant progresses to Ground Lesson 4.

STUDY ASSIGNMENT:

FLIGHT INSTRUCTOR TEXTBOOK

Chapter 2, Section B — Focusing on Teaching Methods

STAGE I

GROUND LESSON 4

LESSON REFERENCES:

FLIGHT INSTRUCTOR TEXTBOOK

Chapter 2, Section B — Focusing on Teaching Methods

RECOMMENDED SEQUENCE:

1. Lesson Introduction
2. Class Discussion

LESSON OBJECTIVES:

During this lesson, the applicant will obtain the instructional knowledge of teaching methods, including how to organize material, the typical steps in a ground training lesson, and the various teaching methods. In addition, the applicant will learn about the integrated method of flight instruction, computer-based training, various instructional aids, and common obstacles to learning.

CONTENT:

SECTION B — FOCUSING ON TEACHING METHODS

❑ Organizing Material
❑ Introduction
❑ Attention
❑ Motivation
❑ Overview
❑ Development
❑ Conclusion
❑ Selecting Teaching Methods
❑ Lecture Method
❑ Lecture Styles
❑ Advantages and Disadvantages of the Lecture Method
❑ Cooperative Learning Method
❑ Guided Discussion Method
❑ Demonstration-Performance Method
❑ Telling-and-Doing Technique
❑ Integrated Method of Flight Instruction
❑ Computer-Based Training Method
❑ Using Instructional Aids
❑ Types of Instructional Aids
❑ Test Preparation Material
❑ Future Developments
❑ Obstacles to Learning

COMPLETION STANDARDS:

The applicant will complete Chapter 2B questions with a minimum passing score of 80 percent, and the instructor will review each incorrect response to ensure complete understanding before the applicant progresses to Ground Lesson 5.

STUDY ASSIGNMENT:

FLIGHT INSTRUCTOR TEXTBOOK

Chapter 2, Section C — Designing Effective Lessons

STAGE I

GROUND LESSON 5

LESSON REFERENCES:

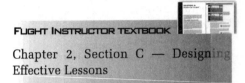

FLIGHT INSTRUCTOR TEXTBOOK

Chapter 2, Section C — Designing Effective Lessons

RECOMMENDED SEQUENCE:
1. Lesson Introduction
2. Class Discussion

LESSON OBJECTIVES:
During this lesson, the applicant will obtain the instructional knowledge of how a course of training is conducted. Specifically, the applicant will become familiar with objectives and standards, blocks of learning, syllabi, and lesson plans, including how to use a lesson plan.

CONTENT:

SECTION C— DESIGNING EFFECTIVE LESSONS
☐ Course of Training
☐ Objectives and Standards

☐ Blocks of Learning
☐ Private Pilot Solo Training
☐ Training ___
☐ Syllabus ___ and Content
☐ How to ___ labus
☐ Lesson Plans
☐ Characteristics of a Well-Planned Lesson
☐ Lesson ___ and Organization
☐ The Po___ roach
☐ How to ___ son Plan

COMPLETION STANDARDS:
The applicant will complete Chapter 2C questions with a minimum passing score of 80 percent, and the instructor will review each incorrect response to ensure complete understanding before the applicant progresses to Ground Lesson 6.

STUDY ASSIGNMENT:

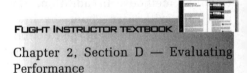

FLIGHT INSTRUCTOR TEXTBOOK

Chapter 2, Section D — Evaluating Performance

STAGE I

GROUND LESSON 6

LESSON REFERENCES:

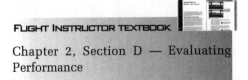

FLIGHT INSTRUCTOR TEXTBOOK

Chapter 2, Section D — Evaluating Performance

RECOMMENDED SEQUENCE:
1. Lesson Introduction
2. Class Discussion

LESSON OBJECTIVES:
During this lesson, the applicant will obtain the instructional knowledge of how to evaluate the performance of a student. Specifically, the applicant will learn about performance evaluations and the various types of critiques.

CONTENT:

SECTION D — EVALUATING PERFORMANCE

- ❏ Critique Versus Evaluation
- ❏ Critiques
- ❏ Characteristics of an Effective Critique
- ❏ Methods of Critiquing
- ❏ Instructor/Student Critique
- ❏ Student-Led Critique
- ❏ Small Group Critique
- ❏ Critique by Another Student
- ❏ Oral Quizzing
- ❏ Written Tests
- ❏ Performance Tests
- ❏ Evaluating Your Own Performance

COMPLETION STANDARDS:

The applicant will complete Chapter 2D questions with a minimum passing score of 80 percent, and the instructor will review each incorrect response to ensure complete understanding before the applicant progresses to Ground Lesson 7.

STUDY ASSIGNMENT:

FLIGHT INSTRUCTOR TEXTBOOK

Chapter 3, Section A — Understanding Human Behavior

STAGE I

GROUND LESSON 7

LESSON REFERENCES:

FLIGHT INSTRUCTOR TEXTBOOK

Chapter 3, Section A — Understanding Human Behavior

GFD FLIGHT INSTRUCTOR VIDEO

Vol I — Human Factors

RECOMMENDED SEQUENCE:

1. Lesson Introduction and Video Presentation
2. Class Discussion

LESSON OBJECTIVES:

In this lesson, the applicant will the instructional knowledge of an behavior and how it applies to a learning environment. Specifically, the applicant will learn about human needs, defense mechanisms, and how students react to stress.

CONTENT:

SECTION A — UNDERSTANDING HUMAN BEHAVIOR

- ❏ Influencing Human Behavior
- ❏ Human Needs
- ❏ Physical
- ❏ Safety
- ❏ Social
- ❏ Ego
- ❏ Self-Fulfillment
- ❏ Defense Mechanisms
- ❏ Compensation
- ❏ Projection

- ❏ Rationalization
- ❏ Denial of Reality
- ❏ Reaction Formation
- ❏ Flight
- ❏ Aggression
- ❏ Resignation
- ❏ Practical Psychology for Flight Instructors
- ❏ Anxiety
- ❏ Normal Reaction to Stress
- ❏ Abnormal Reaction to Stress
- ❏ Psychologically Abnormal Students

COMPLETION STANDARDS:

The applicant will complete Chapter 3A questions with a minimum passing score of 80 percent, and the instructor will review each incorrect response to ensure complete understanding before the applicant progresses to Ground Lesson 8.

STUDY ASSIGNMENT:

FLIGHT INSTRUCTOR TEXTBOOK

Chapter 3, Section B — Making Decisions

STAGE I

GROUND LESSON 8

LESSON REFERENCES:

FLIGHT INSTRUCTOR TEXTBOOK

Chapter 3, Section B — Making Decisions

RECOMMENDED SEQUENCE:

1. Lesson Introduction
2. Class Discussion

LESSON OBJECTIVES:

During this lesson, the applicant will obtain essential knowledge of aeronautical decision making as it is pertains to flight instruction. Specifically, the applicant will learn about the decision making process, risk management, self-assessment, and related factors

concerned with decision making. In addition, the applicant will gain more insight into aviation physiology.

CONTENT:

SECTION B — MAKING DECISIONS

- ❏ Exploring Aeronautical Decision Making (ADM)
- ❏ Applying ADM to Instruction
- ❏ History of ADM
- ❏ Explaining the Decision-Making Process
- ❏ Problem Definition
- ❏ Assessing Risk
- ❏ Creating ADM Lessons
- ❏ Factors Affecting Decision Making
- ❏ Understanding Pilot-In-Command Responsibility
- ❏ Performing Self-Assessment
- ❏ Recognizing Hazardous Attitudes
- ❏ Promoting Communication
- ❏ Describing Resource Use
- ❏ Workload Management

- ❏ Maintaining Situational Awareness
- ❏ Understanding Controlled Flight Into Terrain (CFIT)
- ❏ Identifying Operational Pitfalls
- ❏ Evaluating Student Decision Making
- ❏ Teaching Aviation Physiology
- ❏ Motion Sickness
- ❏ Hypoxia
- ❏ Pressure Effects
- ❏ Scuba Diving
- ❏ Stress
- ❏ Fatigue
- ❏ Noise
- ❏ Alcohol, Drugs, and Performance
- ❏ Fitness for Flight

COMPLETION STANDARDS:

The applicant will complete Chapter 3B questions with a minimum passing score of 80 percent, and the instructor will review each incorrect response to ensure complete understanding before the applicant progresses to Ground Lesson 9.

STUDY ASSIGNMENT:

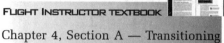

FLIGHT INSTRUCTOR TEXTBOOK

Chapter 4, Section A — Transitioning to the Right Seat

STAGE I

GROUND LESSON 9

LESSON REFERENCES:

FLIGHT INSTRUCTOR TEXTBOOK

Chapter 4, Section A — Transitioning to the Right Seat

GFD FLIGHT INSTRUCTOR VIDEO

Vol II — Transition to the Right Seat

RECOMMENDED SEQUENCE:

1. Lesson Introduction and Video Presentation
2. Class Discussion

LESSON OBJECTIVES:

During this lesson, the applicant will obtain the instructional knowledge of how to operate an airplane from the right seat. Specifically, the applicant will learn techniques for guidance and flight instruction that will be provided to students during flight lessons.

CONTENT:

SECTION A — TRANSITIONING TO THE RIGHT SEAT

- ❏ The Right Seat
- ❏ Orientation
- ❏ Proficiency
- ❏ Practice Instruction
- ❏ Positive Exchange of Flight Controls
- ❏ Use of Distractions
- ❏ Giving Efficient Instruction
- ❏ Insurance and Liability

COMPLETION STANDARDS:

The applicant will complete Chapter 4A questions with a minimum passing score of 80 percent, and the instructor will review each incorrect response to ensure complete understanding before the applicant progresses to Ground Lesson 10.

STUDY ASSIGNMENT:

FLIGHT INSTRUCTOR TEXTBOOK

Chapter 4, Section B, Teaching Flight Safety

STAGE I

GROUND LESSON 10

LESSON REFERENCES:

FLIGHT INSTRUCTOR TEXTBOOK

Chapter 4, Section, B, Teaching Flight Safety

GFD FLIGHT INSTRUCTOR VIDEO

Vol II — Teaching Flight Safety

RECOMMENDED SEQUENCE:

1. Lesson Introduction and Video Presentation
2. Class Discussion

LESSON OBJECTIVES:

During this lesson, the applicant will obtain the instructional knowledge about essential flight safety practices. Specifically, the applicant will learn to analyze weather conditions, preflight activities, ground operations, and inflight operations in relation to how they apply to flight instruction.

CONTENT:

SECTION B — TEACHING FLIGHT SAFETY

- ❑ Preflight Considerations
- ❑ Marginal Weather Judgment Opportunities
- ❑ Ground Operations
- ❑ Checklist Use
- ❑ Propeller Hazards
- ❑ Taxiing
- ❑ Runway Incursion Avoidance
    - ❑ Use of aircraft lighting during taxi and takeoff operations.
    - ❑ Readback/hearback on
        - (1) Hold Short,
        - (2) Position and Hold, and
        - (3) Runway Crossings.
- ❑ Land and Hold Short Operation
- ❑ Airport, Runway, and Taxiway Signs, Lighting, and Markings
- ❑ Wake Turbulence
- ❑ Collision Avoidance
- ❑ Visual Scanning
- ❑ Wind Shear
- ❑ Stall/Spin Awareness
- ❑ Fuel Exhaustion
- ❑ Developing Judgment Skills

COMPLETION STANDARDS:

The applicant will complete Chapter 4B questions with a minimum passing score of 80 percent, and the instructor will review each incorrect response to ensure complete understanding before the applicant progresses to Ground Lesson 11.

STUDY ASSIGNMENT:

FLIGHT INSTRUCTOR TEXTBOOK

Chapter 4, Section C — Developing a Professional Image

STAGE I

GROUND LESSON 1 1

LESSON REFERENCES:

FLIGHT INSTRUCTOR TEXTBOOK

Chapter 4, Section, C, Developing a Professional Image

GFD FLIGHT INSTRUCTOR VIDEO

Vol II — Professionalism

RECOMMENDED SEQUENCE:

1. Lesson Introduction and Video Presentation
2. Class Discussion

LESSON OBJECTIVES:

During this lesson, the applicant will learn what is expected of a professional flight instructor, including qualifications, responsibilities, continuing education requirements, and teaching skills. In addition, prospective applicants will learn more about how to improve their professional image.

CONTENT:

SECTION C — DEVELOPING A PROFESSIONAL IMAGE

❑ Professional Qualifications
❑ Sincerity
❑ Integrity
❑ Credibility
❑ Personal Appearance and Habits
❑ Demeanor
❑ Responsibility to Students
❑ Acceptance of the Student
❑ Proper Language
❑ Reducing Student Frustrations
❑ Become a Positive Role Model
❑ Enhancing Your Qualifications
❑ Expanding Your Technical Knowledge
❑ Building Aeronautical Experience
❑ Improving Teaching Skills
❑ Polishing Your Image

COMPLETION STANDARDS:

The applicant will complete Chapter 4C questions with a minimum passing score of 80 percent, and the instructor will review each incorrect response to ensure complete understanding before the applicant progresses to Ground Lesson 12.

STUDY ASSIGNMENT:

Review appropriate regulations and related publications concerning private and commercial pilot knowledge areas as assigned by the instructor.

STAGE I

GROUND LESSON 1 2

LESSON REFERENCES:

Parts 1, 61, 91, 135,141, NTSB Part 830, the Aeronautical Information Manual, Pertinent Advisory Circulars, and Practical Test Standards (Private and Commercial)

RECOMMENDED SEQUENCE:

1. Lesson Introduction
2. Class Discussion

LESSON OBJECTIVES:

During this lesson, the applicant will obtain the instructional knowledge of the ground training requirements for private and commercial pilots. Specifically, the applicant will review and gain up-to-date knowledge of FAR Part 61, subparts C, E, and F, and FAR Part 141, Appendices B and D, as applicable. The applicant also will review pertinent parts of other aeronautical publications such as the AIM, advisory circulars, and the practical test standards.

CONTENT:

REGULATIONS AND RELATED PUBLICATIONS

❏ FAR Part 1 (Applicable Definitions)
❏ FAR Part 61, Subpart C, Student Pilots
❏ FAR Part 61, Subpart E, Private Pilots
❏ FAR Part 61, Subpart F, Commercial Pilots
❏ FAR Part 91 and 135 (Applicable Sections)

❏ FAR 141, Appendix B, Private Pilot Certification Course
❏ FAR 141, Appendix D, Commercial Pilot Certification Course
❏ NTSB 830
❏ *Aeronautical Information Manual* (Applicable Subjects)
❏ Appropriate FAA Advisory Circulars
❏ Practical Test Standards (Private and Commercial)

COMPLETION STANDARDS:

Through oral quizzing, the instructor will determine that the applicant has obtained the instructional knowledge required to teach the material covered in this lesson before progressing to Ground Lesson 13.

STUDY ASSIGNMENT:

FLIGHT INSTRUCTOR TEXTBOOK

Chapter 4, Section D, Exercising Instructor Privileges

STAGE I

GROUND LESSON 13

LESSON REFERENCES:

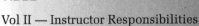

FLIGHT INSTRUCTOR TEXTBOOK

Chapter 4, Section D, Exercising Instructor Privileges

GFD FLIGHT INSTRUCTOR VIDEO

Vol II — Instructor Responsibilities

RECOMMENDED SEQUENCE:

1. Lesson Introduction and Video Presentation
2. Class Discussion

LESSON OBJECTIVES:

During this lesson, the applicant will obtain the instructional knowledge concerning privileges and responsibilities that apply to a certificated flight instructor. Specifically, the applicant will learn about how to provide ground training under Parts 61 and 141. In addition, the applicant will become familiar with required endorsements, record keeping, and knowledge/practical test procedures.

CONTENT:

SECTION D — EXERCISING INSTRUCTOR PRIVILEGES
- ❏ Preparing to Instruct
- ❏ Certificates and Ratings
- ❏ Your Medical Certificate
- ❏ Providing Instruction Under Part 61 and Part 141
- ❏ Aeronautical Knowledge Requirements
- ❏ Home Study Courses
- ❏ Aeronautical Experience Requirements
- ❏ Authorized Instructor
- ❏ Records
- ❏ CFI Renewal
- ❏ Ground Instructors
- ❏ Training the Student Pilot
- ❏ The Student Pilot and Medical Certificates
- ❏ Limitations and Wavers
- ❏ Advising Your Students
- ❏ Medical Application Form
- ❏ Documentation of Training
- ❏ Endorsements
- ❏ Pre-Solo Knowledge Test
- ❏ Solo Privileges
- ❏ Solo Cross-Country
- ❏ Class B Airspace
- ❏ Knowledge Tests
- ❏ Practical Tests
- ❏ The 8710-1 Form
- ❏ Additional Training and Endorsements
- ❏ Preparation
- ❏ Practical Test Standards
- ❏ Satisfactory/Unsatisfactory Performance
- ❏ Recreational Pilots
- ❏ Flight Instructor Training

COMPLETION STANDARDS:
The applicant will complete Chapter 4D questions with a minimum passing score of 80 percent, and the instructor will review each incorrect response to ensure complete understanding before the applicant progresses to Ground Lesson 14.

STUDY ASSIGNMENT:
Review the *Flight Instructor* textbook, Chapters 1 through 4, and other publications as recommended by the flight instructor in preparation for the Stage I Exam.

STAGE I

GROUND LESSON 14

STAGE I EXAM

RECOMMENDED SEQUENCE:
1. Lesson Introduction
2. Testing
3. Critique

LESSON OBJECTIVES:
The exam administered during this lesson evaluates the applicant's comprehension and instructional knowledge of the material presented during this stage of training.

CONTENT:
- ❏ Stage I Exam

COMPLETION STANDARDS:
This lesson and stage are complete when the applicant has completed the

Stage I Exam with a minimum passing score of 80%, and the instructor has reviewed each incorrect response to ensure complete understanding before the applicant progresses to Stage II.

STUDY ASSIGNMENT:

FLIGHT INSTRUCTOR TEXTBOOK

Chapter 5, Section A — Presenting Private Knowledge

STAGE II

STAGE OBJECTIVES

During Stage II, the applicant will begin to apply the principles of planning and organizing ground and flight training lessons. The applicant will acquire practical experience by conducting practice ground training lessons. In addition, the applicant will obtain the instructional knowledge required to teach private and commercial pilot students, including recognition, analysis, and correction of common student errors.

STAGE COMPLETION STANDARD

This Stage is complete when the applicant has completed the Stage II Exam, as well as the Fundamentals of Instruction and Flight Instructor — Airplane End-of-Course Exams, with a minimum passing score of 80 percent, and the instructor has reviewed each incorrect response to ensure complete understanding.

STAGE II

GROUND LESSON 15

LESSON REFERENCES:

FLIGHT INSTRUCTOR TEXTBOOK

Chapter 5, Section A — Presenting Private Knowledge

GFD FLIGHT INSTRUCTOR VIDEO

Vol III — Ground Operations, Basic Maneuvers, Airport Operations, and Emergency Landing Procedures

RECOMMENDED SEQUENCE:

1. Lesson Introduction and Video Presentation
2. Class Discussion

LESSON OBJECTIVES:

During this lesson, the applicant will obtain the instructional knowledge of how to teach the private student. Specifically, the applicant will become familiar with ways to teach airplane systems, basic aerodynamics, performance data, airspace, radio procedures, and weather-related information.

CONTENT:

SECTION A — PRESENTING PRIVATE KNOWLEDGE

❑ Teaching the Private Student
❑ Explaining Airplane Systems
❑ Powerplants
❑ Troubleshooting Problems
❑ Introducing Aerodynamics
❑ Designing Your Own Airplane
❑ Describing Airspace
❑ Practicing Radio Procedures
❑ Predicting Weather
❑ Teaching FARs
❑ Calculating Performance Data

❏ Planning Cross-Country Flights
❏ Private Pilot Aeronautical Decision Making

COMPLETION STANDARDS:

The applicant will complete Chapter 5A questions with a minimum passing score of 80 percent, and the instructor will review each incorrect response to ensure complete understanding before progressing to Ground Lesson 16.

STUDY ASSIGNMENT:

FLIGHT INSTRUCTOR TEXTBOOK

Chapter 5, Section B, Building Flight Skills

STAGE II

GROUND LESSON 16

LESSON REFERENCES:

FLIGHT INSTRUCTOR TEXTBOOK

Chapter 5 — Section B — Building Flight Skills

GFD FLIGHT INSTRUCTOR VIDEO

Vol III — Flight Maneuvers, Ground Reference Maneuvers, Performance Takeoffs and Landings, and Special Flight Operations.

RECOMMENDED SEQUENCE:

1. Lesson Introduction and Video Presentation
2. Class Discussion

LESSON OBJECTIVES:

During this lesson, the applicant will obtain the instructional knowledge required to teach the private student. Specifically, the applicant will learn to teach ground operations, private pilot flight maneuvers, emergency operations, airport operations, takeoffs and landings, preparation for the first solo, performance takeoffs and landings, night flying, instrument flying, cross-country procedures, and preparation for the practical test.

CONTENT:

SECTION B — BUILDING FLIGHT SKILLS
❏ Instructing the Student Pilot
❏ Introducing Ground Operations
❏ Locating The Practice Area
❏ Teaching Private Pilot Maneuvers
❏ Performing Basic Maneuvers
❏ Performing Flight Maneuvers
❏ Flying Ground Reference Maneuvers
❏ Accomplishing Emergency Procedures
❏ Conducting Airport Operations
❏ Operating in the Traffic Pattern
❏ Taking Off
❏ Landing
❏ Flying Solo
❏ Executing Performance Takeoffs and Landings

- Introducing Special Flight Operations
- Flying at Night
- Using Instrument References
- Teaching Cross-Country Flying
- Preparing for the Practical Test

COMPLETION STANDARDS:
The applicant will complete Chapter 5B questions with a minimum passing score of 80 percent, and the instructor

will review each incorrect response to ensure complete understanding before progressing to Ground Lesson 17.

STUDY ASSIGNMENT:

FLIGHT INSTRUCTOR TEXTBOOK

Chapter 5, Section C — Imparting Commercial Knowledge

STAGE II

GROUND LESSON 17

LESSON REFERENCES:

FLIGHT INSTRUCTOR TEXTBOOK

Chapter 5, Section C — Imparting Commercial Knowledge

GFD FLIGHT INSTRUCTOR VIDEO

Vol IV — Advanced Systems

RECOMMENDED SEQUENCE:
1. Lesson Introduction and Video Presentation
2. Class Discussion

LESSON OBJECTIVES:
During this lesson, the applicant will obtain the instructional knowledge of how to teach commercial students. Specifically, the applicant will review and gain up-to-date information on commercial pilot privileges, advanced aerodynamics, performance data, systems, and commercial decision making,

including crew resource management and situational awareness.

CONTENT:

SECTION C — IMPARTING COMMERCIAL KNOWLEDGE
- Teaching the Commercial Student
- Introducing Advanced Systems
- High Performance Powerplants
- Constant-Speed Propellers
- Retractable Landing Gear
- Environmental Systems
- Oxygen Systems
- Cabin Pressurization
- Ice Control Systems
- Exploring Aerodynamics
- High Lift Devices
- High Drag Devices
- High Speed/High Altitude Flight
- Planning Flights
- Commercial Pilot ADM

COMPLETION STANDARDS:
The applicant will complete Chapter 5C questions with a minimum passing score of 80 percent, and the instructor will review each incorrect response to ensure complete understanding before progressing to Ground Lesson 18.

STUDY ASSIGNMENT:
Prepare a ground training lesson on the subjects assigned by the instructor.

Stage II

Ground
Lesson 18

Lesson References:

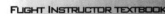

Flight Instructor Textbook

Chapter 1 — Foundations of Learning, and Chapter 2 — The Art and Science of Teaching

Recommended Sequence:
1. Lesson Introduction
2. Class Discussion

Lesson Objectives:
During this lesson, the applicant will learn to conduct a comprehensive ground training lesson which uses instructional aids other than audiovisual materials.

Content:
Conduct the assigned ground training lesson.

Completion Standards:
This lesson is complete when the applicant demonstrates the ability to adhere to a preplanned lesson and communicates effectively without the use of audiovisual materials. At the completion of the lesson, the instructor will evaluate and critique the applicant's presentation and make specific suggestions for improvement.

Study Assignment:
Prepare a ground training lesson on the subjects assigned by the instructor.

Stage II

Ground
Lesson 19

Lesson References:

Flight Instructor Textbook

Chapter 2 — The Art and Science of Teaching, and Chapter 3 — Exploring Human Factors

Recommended Sequence:
1. Lesson Introduction
2. Class Discussion

Lesson Objectives:
During this lesson, the applicant will learn to conduct a comprehensive ground training lesson which uses instructional aids including audiovisual material.

Content:
Conduct the assigned ground training lesson, demonstrating organization of the subject material and proficiency in the transition from one subject to another.

Completion Standards:
This lesson is complete when the applicant demonstrates the ability to adhere to a preplanned lesson and communicates effectively using instructional

aids including audiovisual materials. At the completion of the lesson, the instructor will evaluate and critique the applicant's presentation and make specific suggestions for improvement.

STUDY ASSIGNMENT:

FLIGHT INSTRUCTOR TEXTBOOK

Chapter 5 — Section D, Enhancing Flight Skills

STAGE II

GROUND LESSON 20

LESSON REFERENCES:

FLIGHT INSTRUCTOR TEXTBOOK

Chapter 5 — Section D, Enhancing Flight Skills

GFD FLIGHT INSTRUCTOR VIDEO

Vol IV — Commercial Maneuvers

RECOMMENDED SEQUENCE:

1. Lesson Introduction and Video Presentation
2. Class Discussion

LESSON OBJECTIVES:

During this lesson, the applicant will obtain instructional knowledge on how to teach commercial student pilot skills. Specifically, the applicant will learn how to instruct commercial pilot students in the operation of complex aircraft systems and in the performance of commercial pilot maneuvers.

CONTENT:

SECTION D — ENHANCING FLIGHT SKILLS

❏ Instructing the Commercial Student
❏ Teaching in Complex Airplanes
❏ Retractable Landing Gear
❏ Constant-Speed Propeller Operation
❏ Teaching Commercial Pilot Maneuvers
❏ Perfecting Steep Turns
❏ Performing Chandelles
❏ Flying Lazy Eights
❏ Executing Eights-on-Pylons
❏ Executing Steep Spirals
❏ Performing Power-Off 180° Accuracy Approaches and Landings
❏ Refining Emergency Procedures
❏ Conducting the Long Cross-Country Flight

COMPLETION STANDARDS:

The applicant will complete Chapter 5D questions with a minimum passing score of 80 percent, and the instructor will review each incorrect response to ensure complete understanding before progressing to Ground Lesson 21.

STUDY ASSIGNMENT:

FLIGHT INSTRUCTOR TEXTBOOK

Chapter 5, Section E — Providing Specialized Instruction

STAGE II

GROUND LESSON 21

LESSON REFERENCES:

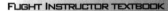

FLIGHT INSTRUCTOR TEXTBOOK

Chapter 5, Section E — Providing Specialized Instruction

GFD FLIGHT INSTRUCTOR VIDEO

Vol IV — Specialized Instruction

RECOMMENDED SEQUENCE:

1. Lesson Introduction and Video Presentation
2. Class Discussion

LESSON OBJECTIVES:

During this lesson, the applicant will obtain the instructional knowledge of lesson content necessary for special instruction. Specifically, the applicant will become familiar with the basic requirements and procedures for providing specialized instruction, including flight reviews, instrument proficiency checks, and various checkouts or transitions.

CONTENT:

SECTION E — PROVIDING SPECIALIZED INSTRUCTION

- ❑ Conducting Flight Reviews
- ❑ Performing Instrument Proficiency Checks
- ❑ Teaching Aircraft Transitions
- ❑ Performing Aircraft Checkouts
- ❑ Complex and High Performance Checkouts
- ❑ Tailwheel Checkouts
- ❑ High-Altitude Checkouts
- ❑ Military to Civilian Transition
- ❑ Instructing in Homebuilt Aircraft
- ❑ Instructing Airline Transport Pilots

COMPLETION STANDARDS:

The applicant will complete Chapter 5E questions with a minimum passing score of 80 percent, and the instructor will review each incorrect response to ensure complete understanding before progressing to Ground Lesson 22.

STUDY ASSIGNMENT:

Prepare a ground training lesson on the subjects assigned by the instructor and the

FLIGHT INSTRUCTOR TEXTBOOK

Chapter 5, Section F — Preparing Future Flight Instructors

STAGE II

GROUND LESSON 22

LESSON REFERENCES:

FLIGHT INSTRUCTOR TEXTBOOK

Chapter 5, Section F — Preparing Future Flight Instructors.

RECOMMENDED SEQUENCE:
1. Lesson Introduction
2. Class Discussion

LESSON OBJECTIVES:
During this lesson, the applicant will conduct a comprehensive ground training lesson using instructional aids where appropriate. The applicant will include all elements of the subjects presented and demonstrate acceptable organization. The applicants also will gain instructional knowledge of how to teach future flight instructors. Specifically, the applicant will review ground instruction requirements, FOI material, and practice ground and flight lessons, including emergency procedures and spin training.

CONTENT:
Conduct a ground training lesson as assigned by the instructor.

SECTION F — PREPARING FUTURE FLIGHT INSTRUCTORS
- ❏ Who Should Become a Flight Instructor?
- ❏ Ground Instruction
- ❏ Fundamentals of Instruction
- ❏ Practice Lessons
- ❏ FARs and Endorsements
- ❏ Flight Instruction
- ❏ Practice Instruction
- ❏ Aeronautical Decision Making
- ❏ Landings
- ❏ Human Factors For CFI Applicants
- ❏ Applying Human Factors Knowledge
- ❏ Stall/Spin Awareness Training
- ❏ Ground Training
- ❏ Demonstration Stalls
- ❏ Spin Training
- ❏ Spin Aerodynamics
- ❏ Spin Training Sequence
- ❏ Spin Limitations
- ❏ Certification Category
- ❏ Safe Altitude
- ❏ Parachutes and Spin Training

COMPLETION STANDARDS:
This lesson is complete when the applicant demonstrates the ability to adhere to a preplanned lesson and effectively communicate the material contained in the lesson. The applicant will also demonstrate the ability to select the most effective instructional aid for the material presented. The instructor will evaluate and critique the applicant's presentation and make specific suggestions for improvement. In addition, the applicant will complete Chapter 5F questions with a minimum passing score of 80 percent, and the instructor will review each incorrect response to ensure complete understanding before the applicant progresses to Ground Lesson 23.

STUDY ASSIGNMENT:
Prepare a ground training lesson as assigned by the instructor and review appropriate regulations/publications related to CFI privileges and limitations, also as assigned by the instructor.

STAGE II

GROUND LESSON 23

LESSON REFERENCES:

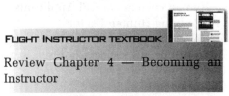

FLIGHT INSTRUCTOR TEXTBOOK

Review Chapter 4 — Becoming an Instructor

Part 61, Subpart H, Flight Instructors

RECOMMENDED SEQUENCE:
1. Lesson Introduction
2. Class Discussion

LESSON OBJECTIVES:
During this lesson, the applicant will conduct a ground training lesson on the subjects assigned by the instructor. The applicant will strive to correct any deficiencies noted in previous ground instruction sessions and increase the overall effectiveness of the presentation. In addition, the applicant will review the regulations that specifically apply to flight instructors.

CONTENT:
Conduct a ground training lesson as assigned by the instructor.

FAR PART 61, SUBPART H, FLIGHT INSTRUCTORS
❑ Applicability
❑ Eligibility Requirements
❑ Aeronautical Knowledge
❑ Flight Proficiency
❑ Flight Instructor Records
❑ Additional Flight Instructor Ratings
❑ Flight Instructor Privileges
❑ Flight Instructor Limitations and Qualifications
❑ Renewal of Flight Instructor Certificates
❑ Expired Flight Instructor Certificates and Ratings

COMPLETION STANDARDS:
This lesson is complete when the applicant demonstrates the ability to adhere to a preplanned lesson and effectively communicate the material contained in the lesson. The instructor will evaluate and critique the applicant's presentation and make specific suggestions for improvement. In addition, through oral quizzing, the instructor will determine that the applicant has obtained the necessary instructional knowledge to teach the assigned regulations.

STUDY ASSIGNMENT:
Complete preparation for the Fundamentals of Instruction Pilot Briefing.

STAGE II

GROUND LESSON 24

PILOT BRIEFING

LESSON REFERENCES:

FLIGHT INSTRUCTOR TEXTBOOK

Chapter 1 — Foundations of Learning, Chapter 2 — The Art and Science of Teaching, Chapter 3 — Exploring Human Factors, and the Fundamentals of Instruction Pilot Briefing

RECOMMENDED SEQUENCE:
1. Lesson Introduction
2. Class Discussion

LESSON OBJECTIVES:
Prior to this lesson, the applicant will formulate comprehensive answers to the essay questions contained in the Fundamentals of Instruction Pilot Briefing using appropriate references. During the discussion, the applicant will explain the answers given and demonstrate that the material is thoroughly understood. The applicant will demonstrate the ability to apply this knowledge to basic flight instruction.

CONTENT:

FUNDAMENTALS OF INSTRUCTION
❑ The Learning Process
❑ The Teaching Process
❑ Planning and Organizing

COMPLETION STANDARDS:
The applicant will demonstrate the understanding of the fundamentals of instruction at a level that ensures that the teaching process can take place effectively. The instructor will review each incorrect response to ensure complete understanding.

STUDY ASSIGNMENT:
Complete preparation for the Flight Instructor Oral Questions Pilot Briefing and the Stage II Exam.

STAGE II

GROUND LESSON 25

PILOT BRIEFING AND STAGE II EXAM

LESSON REFERENCES:

FLIGHT INSTRUCTOR TEXTBOOK

Chapter 1, Foundations of learning, Chapter 2, The Art and Science of Teaching, Chapter 3, Exploring Human Factors, and the Flight Instructor Oral Questions Pilot Briefing

RECOMMENDED SEQUENCE:
1. Lesson Introduction
2. Class Discussion
3. Testing
4. Critique

LESSON OBJECTIVES:
Prior to this lesson, the applicant will formulate comprehensive answers to the essay questions contained in the Flight Instructor Oral Questions Pilot Briefing using appropriate references. During the discussion, the applicant will explain the answers given and demonstrate that the material is thoroughly understood. The applicant will demonstrate the ability to apply this knowledge to flight instruction in preparation for the FOI and end-of-course

final exams. The exam administered during this lesson evaluates the applicant's comprehension and instructional knowledge of the material presented during this stage of training.

CONTENT:

FLIGHT INSTRUCTOR ORAL QUESTIONS

❑ Aerodynamics of Flight
❑ Basic Maneuvers
❑ Soft-Field and Short-Field Takeoffs and Landings
❑ Advanced Maneuvers
❑ Emergency Operations
❑ General Subjects
❑ Stage II Exam

COMPLETION STANDARDS:

The applicant will demonstrate the understanding of the concepts pre-sented in the Pilot Briefing at a level that ensures that the teaching process can take place effectively. In addition, the applicant will complete the Stage II Exam with a minimum passing score of 80 percent, and the instructor will review each incorrect response to ensure complete understanding before the student progresses to Stage III.

STUDY ASSIGNMENT:

FLIGHT INSTRUCTOR TEXTBOOK

Chapters 1, 2, and 3, as necessary, in preparation for the Fundamentals of Instruction Final Examination.

STAGE II

GROUND LESSON 26

LESSON REFERENCES:

Fundamentals of Instruction Final Exam

RECOMMENDED SEQUENCE:

1. Lesson Introduction
2. Testing
3. Critique

LESSON OBJECTIVES:

This testing session evaluates the applicant's comprehension of the material presented in Stages I and II in preparation for the FAA Fundamentals of Instruction Final Examination.

CONTENT:

Fundamentals of Instruction Final Examination

COMPLETION STANDARDS:

The applicant will complete the Fundamentals of Instruction Final Exam with a minimum passing score of 80 percent, and the instructor will review each incorrect response to ensure complete understanding.

STUDY ASSIGNMENT:

The applicant should review the *Flight Instructor* textbook, regulations, and other related publications in preparation for the Flight Instructor-Airplane End-of-Course Examination.

Stage II

Ground Lesson 27

Lesson References:
Flight Instructor — Airplane End-of-Course Examination

Recommended Sequence:
1. Lesson Introduction
2. Testing
3. Critique

Lesson Objectives:
This testing session evaluates the applicant's comprehension of the material presented in Stages I and II of the flight instructor course in preparation for the FAA Flight Instructor — Airplane End-of-Course Examination.

Content:
Flight Instructor — Airplane End-of-Course Examination

Completion Standards:
The applicant will complete the Flight Instructor — Airplane End-of-Course Exam with a minimum passing score of 80 percent, and the instructor will review each incorrect response to ensure complete understanding

Study Assignment:
The flight instructor may assign additional review and study to the applicant in preparation for the FAA Airmen Knowledge and Practical Tests, if appropriate.

FLIGHT INSTRUCTOR
FLIGHT TRAINING SYLLABUS
STAGE I

STAGE OBJECTIVES

During this stage, the applicant will learn the analysis and performance of all the maneuvers required for private and commercial pilot certification from the right seat of the training airplane. Appropriate maneuvers and procedures will be practiced using visual and instrument references, as indicated in the lesson content. Throughout the course, the applicant will use proper single-pilot resource management (SRM) techniques, exhibit positive exchange of aircraft control procedures, and display sound aeronautical decision making (ADM) skills.

STAGE COMPLETION STANDARDS

The applicant must successfully complete each of the lessons in Stage I and demonstrate the use of proper SRM procedures, including the positive exchange of flight controls and effective ADM skills. Additionally, the applicant will be able to analyze and perform all maneuvers from the right seat of the airplane in accordance with the criteria set forth in the current FAA private pilot, commercial pilot, and flight instructor practical test standards, as appropriate.

NOTE: *Students should read Chapter 4, Section A, in the Flight Instructor textbook prior to Flight Lesson 1.*

STAGE I

FLIGHT LESSON 1

DUAL

LESSON OBJECTIVES:

During this lesson, the applicant will learn the fundamentals of analyzing and performing the listed flight maneuvers and procedures and become familiar with the new visual perspectives used when flying in the right seat of the airplane. The applicant will discuss how the use of checklists is an essential element of effective resource use and workload management.

CONTENT:

LESSON INTRODUCTION

PREFLIGHT PREPARATION
❏ Certificates and Documents
❏ Weather Information
❏ National Airspace System
❏ Operation of Systems
❏ Performance and Limitations
❏ Aeromedical Factors
❏ Airworthiness Requirements

PREFLIGHT PROCEDURES
❏ Preflight Inspection
❏ Single-Pilot Resource Management
❏ Use of Checklists
❏ Positive Exchange of Flight Controls

☐ Engine Starting
☐ Before Takeoff Check

AIRPORT OPERATIONS
☐ Radio Communication and ATC Light Signals
☐ Airport, Runway, and Taxiway Signs, Markings, and Lighting
☐ Runway Incursion Avoidance
  ☐ Use of aircraft lighting during taxi and takeoff operations.
  ☐ Readback/hearback on
    (1) Hold Short,
    (2) Position and Hold, and
    (3) Runway Crossings.
☐ Land and Hold Short Operations (LAHSO)

TAXIING
☐ Normal
☐ Crosswind

TAKEOFFS AND CLIMBS
☐ Normal
☐ Crosswind

TRAFFIC PATTERNS

BASIC MANEUVERS
☐ Straight-and-Level Flight
☐ Level Turns
☐ Straight Climbs and Climbing Turns
☐ Straight Descents and Descending Turns

BASIC INSTRUMENT MANEUVERS
☐ Straight-and-Level Flight
☐ Constant Airspeed Climbs
☐ Constant Airspeed Descents
☐ Turns to Headings

☐ Recovery from Unusual Flight Attitudes
☐ Navigation Aids and Radar Services

GROUND REFERENCE MANEUVERS
☐ Rectangular Course
☐ S-Turns
☐ Turns Around a Point

APPROACHES AND LANDINGS
☐ Normal
☐ Crosswind

POSTFLIGHT PROCEDURES
☐ After Landing
☐ Parking and Securing

COMPLETION STANDARDS:
At the completion of this lesson, the applicant will be able to perform and analyze the proper procedures for conducting the airplane and systems preflight inspection, basic airport operations, and ground reference maneuvers. During airport operations, the applicant will maintain a constant vigilance and awareness of all other traffic. In addition, the applicant will demonstrate the correct entry and execution techniques for the listed maneuvers, including the basic instrument maneuvers.

POSTFLIGHT DISCUSSION AND PREVIEW OF NEXT LESSON

LESSON ASSIGNMENT:
Ground Lessons 2 and 3

STAGE I

FLIGHT LESSON 2

DUAL

LESSON OBJECTIVES:

During this lesson, the applicant will demonstrate the accurate analysis and performance of those maneuvers and procedures listed for review. In addition, the applicant will begin to learn the analysis and performance of maneuvering during slow flight and stalls, as well as slips to a landing. The applicant will explain the importance of maintaining situational awareness to prevent runway incursion incidents.

CONTENT:

LESSON REVIEW

PREFLIGHT PREPARATION

- ❏ Certificates and Documents
- ❏ Weather Information
- ❏ Operation of Systems
- ❏ Performance and Limitations

PREFLIGHT PROCEDURES

- ❏ Preflight Inspection
- ❏ Single-Pilot Resource Management
- ❏ Positive Exchange of Flight Controls
- ❏ Engine Starting
- ❏ Before Takeoff Check

AIRPORT OPERATIONS

- ❏ Radio Communications and ATC Light Signals
- ❏ Airport, Runway, and Taxiway Signs, Markings, and Lighting
- ❏ Runway Incursion Avoidance
  - ❏ Use of aircraft lighting during taxi and takeoff operations.
  - ❏ Readback/hearback on
    - (1) Hold Short,
    - (2) Position and Hold, and
    - (3) Runway Crossings.
- ❏ Land and Hold Short Operations (LAHSO)

TAXIING

- ❏ Normal
- ❏ Crosswind

TAKEOFFS AND CLIMBS

- ❏ Normal
- ❏ Crosswind

TRAFFIC PATTERNS

BASIC MANEUVERS

- ❏ Straight-and-Level Flight
- ❏ Level Turns
- ❏ Straight Climbs and Climbing Turns
- ❏ Straight Descents and Descending Turns

BASIC INSTRUMENT MANEUVERS

- ❏ Straight-and-Level Flight
- ❏ Constant Airspeed Climbs
- ❏ Constant Airspeed Descents
- ❏ Turns to Headings
- ❏ Unusual Attitudes
- ❏ Navigation Aids and Radar Services

GROUND REFERENCE MANEUVERS

- ❏ Rectangular Course
- ❏ S-Turns
- ❏ Turns Around a Point

APPROACHES AND LANDINGS

- ❏ Normal
- ❏ Crosswind

POSTFLIGHT PROCEDURES

- ❏ After Landing
- ❏ Parking and Securing

LESSON INTRODUCTION

MANEUVERING DURING SLOW FLIGHT

STALLS

- ❏ Power On
- ❏ Power Off
- ❏ Crossed-Control Stalls (Demonstration)

(4/07)

- Elevator Trim Stalls (Demonstration)
- Secondary Stalls (Demonstration)
- Use of Distractions
- Accelerated Maneuver Stalls (Demonstration)

FORWARD SLIP TO A LANDING

COMPLETION STANDARDS:
At the completion of this lesson, the applicant will be able to analyze and perform the listed proficiency and demonstration stalls with a minimum loss of altitude. While maneuvering during slow flight, altitude will be maintained within 50 feet and heading maintained within 5° of that assigned. In addition, the applicant will correctly and accurately analyze and perform crosswind takeoffs and landings and slips while maintaining airspeed within five knots of the recommended climb or approach airspeed.

POSTFLIGHT DISCUSSION AND PREVIEW OF NEXT LESSON

LESSON ASSIGNMENT:
Ground Lesson 4

STAGE I
FLIGHT LESSON 3
DUAL

LESSON OBJECTIVES:
During this lesson, the applicant will demonstrate the accurate analysis and performance of those maneuvers listed for review. In addition, the applicant will develop the ability to properly perform the listed takeoffs and climbs, approaches and landings, and go-arounds. The applicant will describe how aeronautical decision making (ADM) principles apply to exercising good judgment when executing takeoffs, landings, and go-arounds.

CONTENT:

LESSON REVIEW
- Preflight Preparation
- Preflight Procedures
- Taxiing
- Normal Takeoff and Climb
- Maneuvering During Slow Flight

GROUND REFERENCE MANEUVERS
- Rectangular Course
- S-Turns
- Turns Around a Point

STALLS
- Power On
- Power Off
- Crossed-Control Stalls (Demonstration)
- Elevator Trim Stalls (Demonstration)
- Secondary Stalls (Demonstration)
- Use of Distractions
- Forward Slip to a Landing
- Accelerated Maneuver Stalls (Demonstration) ←

LESSON INTRODUCTION

TAKEOFFS, LANDINGS, AND GO-AROUNDS/REJECTED LANDING
- Short-Field Takeoff and Maximum Performance Climb
- Soft-Field Takeoff and Climb
- Short-Field Approach and Landing
- Soft-Field Approach and Landing
- Forward Slip to a Landing
- Go-Arounds/Rejected Landing

COMPLETION STANDARDS:

At the completion of this lesson, the applicant will be able to demonstrate the correct procedures for short-field and soft-field takeoffs and climbs, short-field and soft-field approaches and landings, and go-arounds. During the demonstration of short-field takeoffs and maximum performance climbs and approaches and landings, the applicant will maintain airspeed within five knots of the manufacturer's recommendations. While demonstrating the soft-field takeoffs and climbs, the applicant will observe the proper airspeeds and liftoff techniques. During the soft-field landing, airspeed will be maintained within five knots. While performing the go-around/rejected landing, the manufac- turer's recommended airspeed and flap retraction sequence will be used. In addition, the applicant will be able to analyze and perform the elements involved in the performance of each of the review maneuvers and explain how each element is important to the performance of the entire maneuver.

POSTFLIGHT DISCUSSION AND PREVIEW OF NEXT LESSON

LESSON ASSIGNMENT:

Ground Lessons 5 and 6

STAGE I

FLIGHT LESSON 4

DUAL, CROSS-COUNTRY

LESSON OBJECTIVES:

During this lesson, the applicant will demonstrate the analysis and perform- ance of the maneuvers listed for review, including the completion of a cross-coun- try flight. In addition, the applicant will apply the correct emergency procedures. The applicant will demonstrate how situ- ational awareness is maintained during cross-country flight by effectively using resources, proper communication skills, and workload management principles.

CONTENT:

LESSON REVIEW

❑ Preflight Preparation
❑ Preflight Procedures

TAKEOFFS, LANDINGS, AND GO-AROUNDS/REJECTED LANDINGS

❑ Short-Field Takeoff and Climb
❑ Soft-Field Takeoff and Maximum Performance Climb
❑ Short-Field Approach and Landing
❑ Soft-Field Approach and Landing
❑ Go-Arounds/Rejected Landing

GROUND REFERENCE MANEUVERS

LESSON INTRODUCTION

STEEP TURNS

NAVIGATION

❑ Pilotage and Dead Reckoning
❑ Navigation Systems and Radar Services
❑ Diversion
❑ Lost Procedures

COLLISION AVOIDANCE

LOW LEVEL WIND SHEAR

WAKE TURBULENCE AVOIDANCE

EMERGENCY OPERATIONS
- ❏ Emergency Descent
- ❏ Emergency Approach and Landing
- ❏ Systems and Equipment Malfunctions
- ❏ Emergency Equipment and Survival Gear

COMPLETION STANDARDS:
At the completion of this lesson, the applicant will demonstrate the performance of steep turns within 100 feet of assigned altitude and 5° of desired angle of bank. All emergency procedures will be conducted in accordance with the manufacturer's recommenda-tions and safe operating procedures. The applicant also will be able to analyze and perform the elements involved in the performance of each of the listed takeoffs, landings, and go-arounds, and explain how each element is important to the performance of the entire procedure.

POSTFLIGHT DISCUSSION AND PREVIEW OF NEXT LESSON

LESSON ASSIGNMENT:
Ground Lesson 7

STAGE I

FLIGHT LESSON 5

DUAL

LESSON OBJECTIVES:
During this lesson, the applicant will practice the review maneuvers and procedures to learn the analysis and performance of each element required for their performance. Additionally, the applicant will learn the elements required for the performance of those maneuvers listed for introduction.

CONTENT:

LESSON REVIEW

PREFLIGHT PREPARATION

PREFLIGHT PROCEDURES

TRAFFIC PATTERNS

NAVIGATION

EMERGENCY OPERATIONS
- ❏ Emergency Descent ←
- ❏ Emergency Approach and Landing
- ❏ Systems and Equipment Malfunctions
- ❏ Emergency Equipment and Survival Gear

LESSON INTRODUCTION
- ❏ Chandelles
- ❏ Lazy Eights
- ❏ Eights-on-Pylons
- ❏ Steep Spirals
- ❏ Power-Off 180° Accuracy Approaches and Landings

COMPLETION STANDARDS:

At the completion of this lesson, the applicant will demonstrate the proper entry and recovery for chandelles, lazy eights, eights-on-pylons, steep spirals, and power-off 180° accuracy approaches and landings. During the chandelle, the applicant will maintain coordination and complete the maneuver within 10° of the desired heading and within five knots of the power-on stalling speed. Lazy eights will be conducted smoothly using proper coordination and symmetrical loops. The applicant will correctly perform and analyze the elements of each of the review maneuvers and procedures and will be able to explain how each element is important to the performance of the entire maneuver or procedure.

POSTFLIGHT DISCUSSION AND PREVIEW OF NEXT LESSON

LESSON ASSIGNMENT:

Ground Lessons 8 and 9

STAGE I

FLIGHT LESSON 6

DUAL

LESSON OBJECTIVES:

During this lesson, the applicant will learn the fundamentals of the analysis and performance of the elements of each of the listed maneuvers and procedures in a complex airplane. In addition, the applicant will discuss ADM principles, such as workload management, which apply when transitioning to complex airplanes.

CONTENT:

LESSON REVIEW
❑ Preflight Preparation
❑ Preflight Procedures
❑ Use of Checklists

TAXIING
❑ Normal
❑ Crosswind

TAKEOFFS AND CLIMBS
❑ Normal
❑ Crosswind
❑ Short-Field
❑ Soft-Field

APPROACHES AND LANDINGS
❑ Normal
❑ Crosswind
❑ Short-Field
❑ Soft-Field

GO-AROUNDS/REJECTED LANDING

CHANDELLES

LAZY EIGHTS

EIGHTS-ON-PYLONS

STEEP SPIRALS

POWER-OFF 180° ACCURACY APPROACHES AND LANDINGS

EMERGENCY OPERATIONS
❑ Emergency Descent ◄
❑ Emergency Approach and Landing
❑ Systems and Equipment Malfunctions
❑ Emergency Equipment and Survival Gear

COMPLETION STANDARDS:
At the completion of this lesson, the applicant will be able to analyze and perform each of the listed maneuvers and procedures, in a complex airplane, at a proficiency level which meets or exceeds that outlined in the current FAA commercial pilot practical test standards. The applicant also will exhibit basic aeronautical decision making and judgment skills.

POSTFLIGHT DISCUSSION AND PREVIEW OF NEXT LESSON

LESSON ASSIGNMENT:
Ground Lessons 10, 11, and 12

STAGE I

FLIGHT LESSON 7

DUAL

LESSON OBJECTIVES:
During this lesson, the applicant will learn the fundamentals of the analysis and performance of the elements associated with night flight operations and basic instrument maneuvers. The applicant also will gain additional knowledge regarding the ADM principles which apply to night operations and basic instrument flight.

CONTENT:

LESSON INTRODUCTION

NIGHT OPERATIONS
❏ Night Preparation
❏ Night Flight
❏ Lighting and Equipment for Night Flying
❏ Physiological Aspects of Night Flying
❏ Preflight Inspection
❏ Engine Starting Procedures
❏ Use of Position and Anti-collision Lights
❏ Taxiing and Orientation
❏ Traffic Patterns

TAKEOFFS AND CLIMBS
❏ Normal
❏ Crosswind

INFLIGHT ORIENTATION

EMERGENCY OPERATIONS

APPROACHES AND LANDINGS
❏ Normal
❏ Crosswind
❏ With and Without Landing Light(s)

GO-AROUNDS/REJECTED LANDINGS

POSTFLIGHT PROCEDURES

LESSON REVIEW

BASIC INSTRUMENT MANEUVERS
❏ Straight-and-Level Flight
❏ Constant Airspeed Climbs
❏ Constant Airspeed Descents
❏ Turns to Headings
❏ Recovery from Unusual Flight Attitudes
❏ Navigation Aids and Radar Services

AERONAUTICAL DECISION MAKING AND RISK MANAGEMENT

COMPLETION STANDARDS:

At the completion of this lesson, the applicant will be able to analyze and perform the elements associated with night flight operations and the listed instrument maneuvers at a proficiency level that meets or exceeds that of a commercial pilot. In addition, the applicant will exhibit sound aeronautical decision making skills.

POSTFLIGHT DISCUSSION AND PREVIEW OF NEXT LESSON

LESSON ASSIGNMENT:

Ground Lessons 13 and 14

STAGE I

FLIGHT LESSON 8

DUAL — STAGE CHECK

LESSON OBJECTIVES:

This flight lesson is a stage check, conducted by the chief instructor, the assistant chief, or a designated check Instructor, to evaluate the applicant's ability to correctly analyze and safely perform the listed maneuvers and procedures. In addition, the applicant's ability to apply the ADM principles of pilot-in-command responsibility, communication, workload management, resource use, and situational awareness to ground and flight operations will be evaluated.

CONTENT:

LESSON REVIEW

PREFLIGHT PREPARATION

PREFLIGHT PROCEDURES

TAXIING
- ❏ Normal
- ❏ Crosswind

AIRPORT OPERATIONS
- ❏ Traffic Patterns

TAKEOFFS AND CLIMBS
- ❏ Normal
- ❏ Crosswind
- ❏ Short-Field
- ❏ Soft-Field

APPROACHES AND LANDINGS
- ❏ Normal
- ❏ Crosswind
- ❏ Short-Field
- ❏ Soft-Field
- ❏ Forward Slip

GO-AROUNDS/REJECTED LANDINGS

NAVIGATION

EMERGENCY OPERATIONS

BASIC INSTRUMENT MANEUVERS
- ❏ Straight-and-Level Flight
- ❏ Constant Airspeed Climbs
- ❏ Constant Airspeed Descents
- ❏ Turns to Headings
- ❏ Recovery from Unusual Flight Attitudes
- ❏ Navigation Aids and Radar Services

RECTANGULAR COURSE

S-TURNS

TURNS AROUND A POINT

EIGHTS-ON-PYLONS

STEEP TURNS

CHANDELLES

LAZY EIGHTS

STEEP SPIRALS

POWER-OFF 180°
ACCURACY APPROACHES
AND LANDINGS

MANEUVERING DURING
SLOW FLIGHT

STALLS
❑ Power On
❑ Power Off
❑ Crossed-Control Stalls
  (Demonstration)
❑ Elevator Trim Stalls
  (Demonstration)
❑ Secondary Stalls (Demonstration)
❑ Use of Distractions
❑ Accelerated Maneuver Stalls
  (Demonstration)

AERONAUTICAL DECISION
MAKING AND RISK
MANAGEMENT

POSTFLIGHT PROCEDURES

COMPLETION STANDARDS:
At the completion of this lesson, the applicant will demonstrate the performance of each of the listed maneuvers and procedures at a proficiency level which meets or exceeds those criteria outlined in the current FAA commercial pilot practical test standards. For those maneuvers and procedures listed only in the FAA private pilot practical test standards, the applicant will be more precise than the standards outlined. Additionally, the applicant will be able to correctly analyze the elements associated with the performance of each maneuver and procedure. Finally, the applicant will perform the listed demonstration stalls, explain associated performance elements, and exhibit sound ADM and judgment skills.

POSTFLIGHT DISCUSSION
AND PREVIEW OF NEXT
LESSON

LESSON ASSIGNMENT:
Ground Lessons 15 and 16

STAGE II

STAGE OBJECTIVES

During this stage, the applicant will acquire the instructional knowledge of the elements of each of the listed maneuvers and procedures including the recognition, analysis, and correction of common student errors. The applicant will be able to prepare a lesson plan for each flight in Stage II and will be able to conduct the flight according to the planned lesson, including effective preflight and postflight instruction.

STAGE COMPLETION STANDARDS

The applicant must successfully complete each of the lessons in Stage II. At the completion of this stage, the applicant will have the proficiency and instructional knowledge of a competent flight instructor with an airplane category rating and a single-engine class rating. This proficiency level will meet or exceed the criteria of the private pilot, commercial pilot, and flight instructor practical test standards, as appropriate.

STAGE II

FLIGHT LESSON 9

DUAL

LESSON OBJECTIVES:

During this lesson, the applicant will obtain the instructional knowledge of the elements of each of the listed maneuvers and procedures and of the common errors, including the recognition, analysis, and correction. The applicant also will demonstrate the ability to incorporate ADM principles into flight lessons. For example, the use of checklists can be emphasized as an important resource used to enhance a student's ability to manage workload.

CONTENT:

LESSON INTRODUCTION

PREFLIGHT PREPARATION
❏ Certificates and Documents

❏ Weather Information
❏ National Airspace System
❏ Operation of Systems
❏ Performance and Limitations
❏ Aeromedical Factors
❏ Airworthiness Requirements

PREFLIGHT PROCEDURES
❏ Preflight Inspection
❏ Single-Pilot Resource Management ⏋
❏ Use of Checklists
❏ Positive Exchange of Flight Controls

AIRPORT OPERATIONS
❏ Radio Communications and ATC Light Signals
❏ Airport, Runway, and Taxiway Signs, Markings, and Lighting
❏ Runway Incursion Avoidance/ LAHSO
❏ Engine Starting
❏ Before Takeoff Check

TAXIING
❏ Normal
❏ Crosswind

Takeoffs and Climbs
- ❏ Normal
- ❏ Crosswind

Traffic Patterns

Straight-and-Level Flight

Level Turns

Straight Climbs and Climbing Turns

Straight Descents and Descending Turns

Basic Instrument Maneuvers
- ❏ Straight-and-Level Flight
- ❏ Constant Airspeed Climbs
- ❏ Constant Airspeed Descents
- ❏ Turns to Headings
- ❏ Recovery from Unusual Flight Attitudes
- ❏ Navigation Aids and Radar Services

Rectangular Course

S-Turns

Turns Around a Point

Approaches and Landings
- ❏ Normal
- ❏ Crosswind

Postflight Procedures
- ❏ After Landing
- ❏ Parking and Securing

Completion Standards:
At the completion of this lesson, the applicant will be able to analyze and perform each of the listed procedures at the competency level that meets or exceeds the criteria outlined in the current FAA flight instructor practical test standards. In addition, the applicant will demonstrate the instructional knowledge of the elements of the maneuver or procedure, including the recognition, analysis, and correction of common student errors.

Postflight Discussion and Preview of Next Lesson

Lesson Assignment:
Ground Lesson 17

STAGE II

Flight Lesson 10

Dual

Lesson Objectives:
During this lesson, the applicant will practice the review maneuvers and procedures to further develop instructional techniques. In addition, the applicant will obtain the instructional knowledge of the elements of each of the new maneuvers and procedures and of the common errors, including recognition, analysis, and correction. The applicant will demonstrate the ability to present ADM concepts to students, such as the importance of maintaining situational awareness to prevent runway incursion incidents.

Content:

Lesson Review

Preflight Preparation
- ❏ Certificates and Documents
- ❏ Weather Information
- ❏ Operation of Systems
- ❏ Performance and Limitations

PREFLIGHT PROCEDURES
- ❑ Preflight Inspection
- ❑ Single-Pilot Resource Management
- ❑ Use of Checklists
- ❑ Engine Starting
- ❑ Before Takeoff Check

AIRPORT OPERATIONS
- ❑ Radio Communications and ATC Light Signals
- ❑ Airport, Runway, and Taxiway Signs, Markings, and Lighting
- ❑ Runway Incursion Avoidance/ LAHSO

TAXIING
- ❑ Normal
- ❑ Crosswind

TAKEOFFS AND CLIMBS
- ❑ Normal
- ❑ Crosswind

TRAFFIC PATTERNS

STRAIGHT-AND-LEVEL FLIGHT

LEVEL TURNS

STRAIGHT CLIMBS AND CLIMBING TURNS

STRAIGHT DESCENTS AND DESCENDING TURNS

BASIC INSTRUMENT MANEUVERS
- ❑ Straight-and-Level Flight
- ❑ Constant Airspeed Climbs
- ❑ Constant Airspeed Descents
- ❑ Turns to Headings
- ❑ Recovery from Unusual Flight Attitudes
- ❑ Navigation Aids and Radar Services

RECTANGULAR COURSE

S-TURNS

TURNS AROUND A POINT

APPROACHES AND LANDINGS
- ❑ Normal
- ❑ Crosswind

POSTFLIGHT PROCEDURES

LESSON INTRODUCTION

MANEUVERING DURING SLOW FLIGHT

STALLS
- ❑ Power On
- ❑ Power Off
- ❑ Crossed-Control Stalls (Demonstration)
- ❑ Elevator Trim Stalls (Demonstration)
- ❑ Secondary Stalls (Demonstration)
- ❑ Use of Distractions
- ❑ Accelerated Maneuver Stalls (Demonstration)

COMPLETION STANDARDS:
At the completion of this lesson, the applicant will be able to analyze and perform each of the listed maneuvers and procedures at a competency level that meets or exceeds the criteria outlined in the current FAA flight instructor practical test standards. In addition, the applicant will demonstrate the instructional knowledge of the elements of the maneuver or procedure, including the recognition, analysis, and correction of common student errors.

POSTFLIGHT DISCUSSION AND PREVIEW OF NEXT LESSON

LESSON ASSIGNMENT:
Ground Lesson 18

STAGE II

FLIGHT LESSON 11

DUAL

LESSON OBJECTIVES:
During this lesson, the applicant will practice the review maneuvers and procedures to further develop instruction techniques. In addition, the applicant will obtain the instructional knowledge of the elements of each of the new maneuvers and procedures and of the common errors, including recognition, analysis, and correction. The applicant will demonstrate how the practice of ADM principles can be included in lessons covering takeoffs, landings, and go-arounds.

CONTENT:

LESSON REVIEW

PREFLIGHT PREPARATION

PREFLIGHT PROCEDURES

TAXIING

NORMAL TAKEOFFS AND CLIMBS

MANEUVERING DURING SLOW FLIGHT

STALLS
❑ Power-On
❑ Power-Off

LESSON INTRODUCTION

COLLISION AVOIDANCE

LOW LEVEL WIND SHEAR

WAKE TURBULENCE AVOIDANCE

TAKEOFFS, LANDINGS, AND GO-AROUNDS/REJECTED LANDINGS
❑ Short-Field Takeoff and Maximum Performance Climb
❑ Soft-Field Takeoff and Climb
❑ Short-Field Approach and Landing
❑ Soft-Field Approach and Landing
❑ Slip to a Landing
❑ Go-Arounds/Rejected Landings

COMPLETION STANDARDS:
At the completion of this lesson, the applicant will be able to analyze and perform each of the listed maneuvers and procedures at a competency level that meets or exceeds the criteria outlined in the current FAA flight instructor practical test standards. In addition, the applicant will demonstrate the instructional knowledge of the elements of the maneuver or procedure, including the recognition, analysis, and correction of common student errors.

POSTFLIGHT DISCUSSION AND PREVIEW OF NEXT LESSON

LESSON ASSIGNMENT:
Ground Lesson 19

STAGE II

FLIGHT LESSON 12

DUAL

LESSON OBJECTIVES:
During this lesson, the applicant will practice the review maneuvers and procedures to further develop instructional techniques. In addition, the applicant will obtain the instructional knowledge of the elements of each of the new maneuvers and procedures and of the common errors including recognition, analysis, and correction. The applicant will demonstrate methods to incorporate ADM concepts, including workload management, communication, and resource use into lessons involving cross-country flight.

CONTENT:

LESSON REVIEW
❑ Preflight Preparation
❑ Preflight Procedures

TAKEOFFS, LANDINGS AND GO-AROUNDS
❑ Short-Field Takeoff and Maximum Performance Climb
❑ Soft-Field Takeoff and Climb
❑ Short-Field Approach and Landing
❑ Soft-Field Approach and Landing
❑ Go-Around/Rejected Landings

LESSON INTRODUCTION

STEEP TURNS

NAVIGATION
❑ Pilotage and Dead Reckoning
❑ Navigation Systems and ATC Radar Services
❑ Diversion
❑ Lost Procedure

EMERGENCY OPERATIONS
❑ Emergency Descent
❑ Emergency Approach and Landing
❑ Systems and Equipment Malfunctions
❑ Emergency Equipment and Survival Gear

AERONAUTICAL DECISION MAKING AND RISK MANAGEMENT

COMPLETION STANDARDS:
At the completion of this lesson, the applicant will be able to analyze and perform each of the listed maneuvers and procedures at a competency level that meets or exceeds the criteria outlined in the current FAA flight instructor practical test standards. In addition, the applicant will demonstrate the instructional knowledge of the elements of the maneuver or procedure, including the recognition, analysis, and correction of common student errors.

POSTFLIGHT DISCUSSION AND PREVIEW OF NEXT LESSON

LESSON ASSIGNMENT:
Ground Lessons 20 and 21

STAGE II

FLIGHT LESSON 13

DUAL

LESSON OBJECTIVES:
During this lesson, the applicant will practice the review maneuvers and procedures to further develop instructional techniques. In addition, the applicant will obtain the instructional knowledge of the elements of each of the new maneuvers and procedures and of the common errors including recognition, analysis, and correction. Spin entries, spins, and spin recoveries will be introduced. The applicant will address how distractions can lead to a lack of situational awareness and the potential for inadvertent stall/spin incidents.

CONTENT:

LESSON REVIEW
❑ Preflight Preparation
❑ Preflight Procedures
❑ Traffic Patterns
❑ Steep Turns
❑ Navigation

EMERGENCY OPERATIONS
❑ Emergency Approach and Landing
❑ Systems and Equipment Malfunctions
❑ Emergency Equipment and Survival Gear

LESSON INTRODUCTION

CHANDELLES

LAZY EIGHTS

EIGHTS ON PYLONS

STEEP SPIRALS

POWER-OFF 180° ACCURACY APPROACHES AND LANDINGS

STALL/SPIN AWARENESS EXERCISES
❑ Use of Distractions
❑ Spin Entry, Spins, and Spin Recovery
❑ Spins in Both Directions

COMPLETION STANDARDS:
At the completion of this lesson, the applicant will be able to analyze and perform each of the listed maneuvers and procedures at a competency level that meets or exceeds the criteria outlined in the current FAA flight instructor practical test standards. In addition, the applicant will demonstrate the instructional knowledge of the elements of the maneuver or procedure, including the recognition, analysis, and correction of common student errors.

POSTFLIGHT DISCUSSION AND PREVIEW OF NEXT LESSON

LESSON ASSIGNMENT:
Ground Lessons 22 and 23

STAGE II

FLIGHT LESSON 14

DUAL

LESSON OBJECTIVES:
During this lesson, the applicant will obtain the instructional knowledge of the elements of the listed maneuvers and procedures and of the common errors, including recognition, analysis, and correction in a complex airplane. The applicant will conduct the flight in the role of flight instructor, demonstrating and evaluating the performance of each maneuver.

CONTENT:

LESSON REVIEW
❏ Preflight Preparation
❏ Preflight Procedures

TAXIING
❏ Normal
❏ Crosswind

TAKEOFFS AND CLIMBS
❏ Normal
❏ Crosswind
❏ Short-Field
❏ Soft-Field

APPROACHES AND LANDINGS
❏ Normal
❏ Crosswind
❏ Crosswind
❏ Short-Field
❏ Soft-Field

GO-AROUNDS/REJECTED LANDINGS

CHANDELLES

LAZY EIGHTS

EIGHTS ON PYLONS

STEEP SPIRALS

POWER-OFF 180° ACCURACY APPROACHES AND LANDINGS

STALL/SPIN AWARENESS EXERCISES

EMERGENCY OPERATIONS
❏ Emergency Descent
❏ Emergency Approach and Landing
❏ Systems and Equipment Malfunctions
❏ Emergency Equipment and Survival Gear

HIGH ALTITUDE OPERATIONS

AERONAUTICAL DECISION MAKING AND JUDGMENT

COMPLETION STANDARDS:
At the completion of this lesson, the applicant will be able to analyze and perform each of the listed maneuvers and procedures at a competency level that meets or exceeds the criteria outlined in the current FAA flight instructor practical test standards. In addition, the applicant will demonstrate the instructional knowledge of the elements of the maneuver or procedure, including the recognition, analysis, and correction of common student errors.

POSTFLIGHT DISCUSSION AND PREVIEW OF NEXT LESSON

LESSON ASSIGNMENT:
Ground Lessons 24 and 25

STAGE II

FLIGHT LESSON 15

DUAL

LESSON OBJECTIVES:
During this lesson, the applicant will obtain the instructional knowledge of the elements of night flight operations and of the common errors, including recognition, analysis, and correction. The applicant will demonstrate methods incorporating ADM principles into instruction of night operations and basic instrument flight.

CONTENT:

LESSON INTRODUCTION

NIGHT OPERATIONS
❑ Night Preparation
❑ Night Flight
❑ Lighting and Equipment for Night Flying
❑ Physiological Aspects of Night Flying
❑ Preflight Inspection
❑ Engine Starting Procedures
❑ Use of Position and Anti-collision Lights
❑ Taxiing and Orientation
❑ Traffic Patterns

TAKEOFFS AND CLIMBS
❑ Normal
❑ Crosswind

INFLIGHT ORIENTATION

EMERGENCY OPERATIONS

APPROACHES AND LANDINGS
❑ Normal
❑ Crosswind
❑ With and Without Landing Light(s)

GO-AROUNDS/REJECTED LANDINGS

POSTFLIGHT PROCEDURES

LESSON REVIEW

BASIC INSTRUMENT MANEUVERS
❑ Straight-and-Level Flight
❑ Constant Airspeed Climbs
❑ Constant Airspeed Descents
❑ Turns to Headings
❑ Recovery from Unusual Flight Attitude
❑ Navigation Aids and Radar Services

COMPLETION STANDARDS:
At the completion of this lesson, the applicant will be able to analyze and perform each of the listed maneuvers and procedures at a competency level that meets or exceeds the criteria outlined in the current FAA flight instructor practical test standards. In addition, the applicant will demonstrate the instructional knowledge of the elements of the maneuver or procedure, including the recognition, analysis, and correction of common student errors.

POSTFLIGHT DISCUSSION AND PREVIEW OF NEXT LESSON

LESSON ASSIGNMENT:
Ground Lessons 26 and 27

STAGE II

FLIGHT LESSON 16

DUAL — STAGE CHECK

LESSON OBJECTIVES:
During this lesson, the chief instructor, assistant chief instructor, or a designated check instructor will determine that the applicant meets the proficiency requirements for a flight instructor certificate with an airplane, single-engine class rating.

CONTENT:

LESSON REVIEW

PREFLIGHT PREPARATION

PREFLIGHT PROCEDURES

PREFLIGHT LESSON ON A MANEUVER TO BE PERFORMED IN FLIGHT
❑ Maneuver Lesson

TAXIING
❑ Normal
❑ Crosswind

AIRPORT OPERATIONS
❑ Traffic Patterns

TAKEOFFS AND CLIMBS
❑ Normal
❑ Crosswind
❑ Short-Field
❑ Soft-Field

APPROACHES AND LANDINGS
❑ Normal
❑ Crosswind
❑ Short-Field
❑ Soft-Field
❑ Slip to a landing
❑ Go-Arounds/Rejected Landings

FUNDAMENTALS OF FLIGHT
❑ Straight-and-Level Flight
❑ Level Turns
❑ Straight Climbs and Climbing Turns
❑ Straight Descents and Descending Turns

NAVIGATION

EMERGENCY OPERATIONS

AERONAUTICAL DECISION MAKING AND RISK MANAGEMENT

BASIC INSTRUMENT MANEUVERS
❑ Straight-and-Level Flight
❑ Constant Airspeed Climbs
❑ Constant Airspeed Descents
❑ Turns to Headings
❑ Recovery from Unusual Flight Attitude

RECTANGULAR COURSE

S-TURNS

TURNS AROUND A POINT

EIGHTS ON PYLONS

STEEP TURNS

CHANDELLES

LAZY EIGHTS

STEEP SPIRALS

POWER-OFF 180°

ACCURACY APPROACHES AND LANDINGS

MANEUVERING DURING SLOW FLIGHT

STALL/SPIN AWARENESS EXERCISES
❑ Use of Distractions
❑ Spin Entry, Spins, and Spin Recovery
❑ Spins in Both Directions

STALLS
❑ Power On
❑ Power Off

- Crossed-Control Stalls
  (Demonstration)
- Elevator Trim Stalls (Demonstration)
- Secondary Stalls (Demonstration)
- Accelerated Maneuver Stalls
  (Demonstration)

POSTFLIGHT PROCEDURES

COMPLETION STANDARDS:
At the completion of this lesson, the applicant will demonstrate the skill

and instructional knowledge required to successfully complete the flight instructor practical test. Each maneuver and procedure will be performed at a proficiency level that meets or exceeds the criteria outlined in the current FAA private pilot, commercial pilot, and flight instructor practical test standards, as appropriate.

POSTFLIGHT DISCUSSION AND PREVIEW OF NEXT LESSON

STAGE II

FLIGHT LESSON 17

DUAL — END-OF-COURSE FLIGHT CHECK

LESSON OBJECTIVE
During this lesson, the chief instructor, assistant chief instructor, or a designated check instructor will determine that the applicant meets the knowledge and proficiency requirements for a flight instructor certificate with an airplane, single-engine class rating.

NOTE: *End-of-course flight checks include a broad range of knowledge and skill areas listed in the Flight Instructor Practical Test Standards (PTS). However, since it is impractical to complete all of the listed tasks on one flight check, the end-of-course checks should be conducted as a practical test. According to the practical test concept, an examiner may select specific tasks within an area of operation for testing purposes. Some areas of*

operation contain tasks that require the applicant to demonstrate instructional knowledge, others specify proficiency or demonstration of skill, and in some cases, certain tasks must be evaluated. All instructors and instructor applicants should be familiar with the practical test concept.

CONTENT:

LESSON REVIEW

FUNDAMENTALS OF INSTRUCTING
- The Learning Process
- Human Behavior and Effective Communication
- The Teaching Process
- Teaching Methods
- Critique and Evaluation
- Flight Instructor Characteristics and Responsibilities
- Planning Instructional Activity

TECHNICAL SUBJECT AREAS
- Aeromedical Factors
- Visual Scanning and Collision Avoidance

- ❑ Principles of Flight
- ❑ Airplane Flight Controls
- ❑ Airplane Weight and Balance
- ❑ Navigation and Flight Planning
- ❑ Night Operations
- ❑ High Altitude Operations
- ❑ FARs and Publications
- ❑ Navigation Aids and Radar Services
- ❑ National Airspace System
- ❑ Logbook Entries and Certificate Endorsements

PREFLIGHT PREPARATION
- ❑ Certificates and Documents
- ❑ Weather Information
- ❑ Operations of Systems
- ❑ Performance and Limitations
- ❑ Airworthiness Requirements

PREFLIGHT LESSON ON A MANEUVER TO BE PERFORMED IN FLIGHT
- ❑ Maneuver Lesson

PREFLIGHT PROCEDURES
- ❑ Preflight Inspection
- ❑ Single-Pilot Resource Management
- ❑ Engine Starting
- ❑ Taxiing
- ❑ Before Takeoff Check

AIRPORT OPERATIONS
- ❑ Radio Communications and ATC Light Signals
- ❑ Traffic Patterns
- ❑ Airport, Runway, and Taxiway Signs, Markings, and Lighting
- ❑ Runway Incursion Avoidance/LAHSO

TAKEOFFS, LANDINGS AND GO-AROUNDS/REJECTED LANDINGS
- ❑ Normal and Crosswind Takeoff and Climb
- ❑ Short-Field Takeoff and Maximum Performance Climb
- ❑ Soft-Field Takeoff and Climb
- ❑ Normal and Crosswind Approach and Landing

- ❑ Slip to a Landing
- ❑ Go-Around/Rejected Landing
- ❑ Short-Field Approach and Landing
- ❑ Soft-Field Approach and Landing

FUNDAMENTALS OF FLIGHT
- ❑ Straight-and-Level Flight
- ❑ Level Turns
- ❑ Straight Climbs and Climbing Turns
- ❑ Straight Descents and Descending Turns

SLOW FLIGHT, STALLS AND SPINS
- ❑ Maneuvering During Slow Flight
- ❑ Power-On Stalls (Proficiency)
- ❑ Power-Off Stalls (Proficiency)
- ❑ Crossed-Control Stalls (Demonstration)
- ❑ Elevator Trim Stalls (Demonstration)
- ❑ Secondary Stalls (Demonstration)
- ❑ Accelerated Maneuver Stalls (Demonstration)
- ❑ Spins

BASIC INSTRUMENT MANEUVERS
- ❑ Straight-and-Level Flight
- ❑ Constant Airspeed Climbs
- ❑ Constant Airspeed Descents
- ❑ Turns to Headings
- ❑ Recovery from Unusual Flight Attitudes

PERFORMANCE MANEUVERS
- ❑ Steep Turns
- ❑ Chandelles
- ❑ Lazy Eights
- ❑ Steep Spirals
- ❑ Power-Off 180° Accuracy Approaches and Landings

GROUND REFERENCE MANEUVERS
- ❑ Rectangular Course
- ❑ S-Turns Across a Road

☐ Turns Around a Point
☐ Eights-on-Pylons

EMERGENCY OPERATIONS
☐ Emergency Descent
☐ Emergency Approach and Landing (Simulated)
☐ Systems and Equipment Malfunction
☐ Emergency Equipment and Survival Gear

POSTFLIGHT PROCEDURES
☐ Postflight Procedures

COMPLETION STANDARDS:
At the completion of this lesson, the applicant will demonstrate satisfactory performance according to the appropriate FAA practical test standards with regard to:

1. knowledge of the fundamentals of instructing;
2. knowledge of the technical subject areas;
3. knowledge of the flight instructor's responsibilities concerning the pilot certification process;
4. knowledge of the flight instructor's responsibilities concerning logbook entries and pilot certificate endorsements;
5. ability to demonstrate the procedures and maneuvers selected by the examiner to at least the commercial pilot skill level while giving effective instruction;
6. competence in teaching the procedures and maneuvers selected by the examiner;
7. competence in describing, recognizing, analyzing, and correcting common errors simulated by the examiner; and
8. knowledge of the development and effective use of a course of training, a syllabus, and a lesson plan;
9. competence in incorporating ADM principles into ground and flight lessons.

POSTFLIGHT DISCUSSION

FLIGHT INSTRUCTOR INSTRUMENT CERTIFICATION COURSE

COURSE OBJECTIVES

The applicant will obtain the knowledge, skill, and aeronautical experience necessary to meet the requirements for the addition of an instrument – airplane rating to an existing flight instructor certificate.

COURSE COMPLETION STANDARDS

The applicant will demonstrate through written tests and flight tests, and show through appropriate records, that the knowledge, skill, and experience requirements necessary for the addition of an instrument – airplane rating to an existing flight instructor certificate have been obtained.

GROUND TRAINING COURSE OBJECTIVES

The applicant will obtain the necessary aeronautical knowledge, instructional background, and meet the prerequisites specified in Part 61 for the FAA flight instructor, instrument – airplane airmen knowledge test.

COMPLETION STANDARDS

The applicant will demonstrate, through oral and written tests and records, that the prerequisites specified in Part 61 have been met and the necessary knowledge to pass the FAA flight instructor, instrument – airplane airmen knowledge test examination has been obtained.

FLIGHT TRAINING COURSE OBJECTIVES

The applicant will obtain the aeronautical skill, instructional knowledge, and experience necessary to meet the requirements for the addition of an instrument, airplane rating to an existing flight instructor certificate.

COMPLETION STANDARDS

The applicant will demonstrate, through flight tests and school records, that the aeronautical skill, instructional knowledge, and experience necessary to meet the requirements for the addition of an instrument – airplane rating to an existing flight instructor certificate has been obtained.

Flight Instructor Instrument Certification Course Overview

The following time analysis indicates compliance with Part 141, Appendix G.

MINIMUM COURSE HOURS

	GROUND TRAINING				FLIGHT TRAINING			
	Briefing Sessions	AV and Class Discussion	Stage / End-of-Course Exams	Exam Debriefings	Maneuver Analysis	Practice Instruction	Stage/ End-of-Course Checks	Preflight/ Postflight Briefings
Stage III		6.0	.5	As Req.	6.5		1.5	As Req.
Stage IV	1.0	4.0	3.0	.5		8.5	3.5	As Req.
TOTAL	1.0	10.0	3.5	.5	6.5	8.5	5.0	As Req.

Note: *The times for stage and end-of-course checks are included in the totals for maneuver analysis and practice instruction.*

APPLICANT INFORMATION

COURSE ENROLLMENT
To enroll in the instrument flight instructor course, you must hold a commercial pilot certificate or airline transport pilot certificate with an aircraft category, class, and instrument rating appropriate to the flight instructor category and class rating for which the course applies. In addition, you must hold a flight instructor certificate with an airplane category rating and a single-engine class rating.

REQUIREMENTS FOR GRADUATION
To obtain an instrument flight instructor rating, you must successfully complete all of the ground training and flight training lessons contained in Stages III and IV.

LESSON DESCRIPTION AND STAGES OF TRAINING
Each lesson is fully described within the syllabus, including the objectives, standards, and measurable units of accomplishment and learning for each lesson. The objectives and standards of each stage are described within the syllabus.

TESTS AND CHECKS
The syllabus incorporates stage checks in accordance with Part 141. These checks are given by the chief instructor, the assistant chief instructor, or a designated check instructor at the end of each stage. You also will complete the appropriate stage exams, pilot briefings, and final examinations that are described within the syllabus. In addition, you must satisfactorily accomplish an end-of-course test after all of the stages have been completed.

LESSON TIME ALLOCATION

	Ground Training				Flight Training		
Pilot Briefings	AV Presentation & Class Discussion	Stage & End-of-Course Exam Completion	Stage & End-of-Course Exam Debriefing		Maneuver Analysis	Practice Instruction	Stage/E-O-C Checks
STAGE III							
	1.5			Ground Lesson 28			
				Flight Lesson 18	1.0		
	1.5			Ground Lesson 29			
				Flight Lesson 19	1.0		
	1.0			Ground Lesson 30			
				Flight Lesson 20	1.0		
	1.0			Ground Lesson 31			
				Flight Lesson 21	1.0		
	1.0			Ground Lesson 32			
		.5	As Req.	Ground Lesson 33 – Stage III Exam			
				Flight Lesson 22	1.0		
				Flight Lesson 23 – Stage Check	1.5		1.5
	6.0	.5	As Req.	**Stage Totals**	6.5		1.5
STAGE IV							
	1.0			Ground Lesson 34			
				Flight Lesson 24		1.0	
	1.0			Ground Lesson 35			
				Flight Lesson 25		1.0	
	1.0			Ground Lesson 36			
				Flight Lesson 26		1.0	
	1.0			Ground Lesson 37			
				Flight Lesson 27		1.0	
1.0		.5		Ground Lesson 38 – Briefing and Stage IV Exam			
				Flight Lesson 28		1.0	
		2.5	.5	Ground Lesson 39 – End-of-Course Exam			
				Flight Lesson 29 – Stage Check		1.5	1.5
				Flight Lesson 30 – End-of-Course Check		2.0	2.0
1.0	4.0	3.0	.5	**Stage Totals**		8.5	3.5
1.0	10.0	3.5	.5	**Course Totals**	6.5	8.5	5.0

NOTE: *Individual times shown are for guidance only; they are not mandatory for each lesson. However, the totals in each category should be attained at the completion of each stage to ensure the student will acquire the minimum instruction required by Part 141. Preflight and postflight briefing times are as required.*

INSTRUMENT INSTRUCTOR GROUND TRAINING SYLLABUS
STAGE III

STAGE OBJECTIVES
During Stage III, the applicant will review the principles of attitude instrument flying, ATC procedures, and IFR navigational charts. The applicant will obtain the instructional knowledge required to teach these subjects including the recognition, analysis, and correction of common student errors.

STAGE COMPLETION STANDARDS
This Stage Is complete when the applicant has completed the Instrument Flight Instructor Stage III Exam with a minimum passing score of 80 percent and the instructor has reviewed each incorrect response to ensure complete understanding.

STAGE III

GROUND LESSON 28

LESSON REFERENCES:

FLIGHT INSTRUCTOR TEXTBOOK

Chapter 6, Section A — Conveying Instrument Knowledge

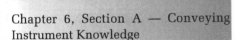

GFD FLIGHT INSTRUCTOR VIDEO

Vol V — Instructing the Instrument Student

RECOMMENDED SEQUENCE:
1. Lesson Introduction and Video Presentation
2. Class Discussion

LESSON OBJECTIVES:
During this lesson, the applicant will review information on learning theories and teaching methods. In addition, the applicant will obtain the instructional knowledge required to teach the use and operation of flight and gyroscopic instruments. The applicant will also obtain the instructional knowledge required to teach basic attitude instrument flying, including common instrument failure indications, partial panel procedures, instrument navigation, charts and chart procedures, and meteorology.

CONTENT:

LESSON REVIEW:

FUNDAMENTALS OF INSTRUCTION
❑ The Learning Process
❑ The Teaching Process
❑ Teaching Methods
❑ Evaluation

- ❏ Flight Instructor Characteristics and Responsibilities
- ❏ Human Factors
- ❏ Planning Instructional Activity

SECTION A — CONVEYING INSTRUMENT KNOWLEDGE

- ❏ Understanding Instruments
- ❏ Attitude Indicator
- ❏ Heading Indicator
- ❏ Turn Indicators
- ❏ Vertical Speed Indicator
- ❏ Airspeed Indicator
- ❏ Attitude Instrument Flying
- ❏ Instrument Cross-Check
- ❏ Instrument Interpretation
- ❏ Aircraft Control
- ❏ Pitot-Static System Failure
- ❏ Gyroscopic Instrument Failure
- ❏ Attitude Indicator Failure
- ❏ Heading Indicator Failure
- ❏ Instrument Navigation
- ❏ Compass and Timed Turns
- ❏ Unusual Attitude Recovery
- ❏ Control and Performance Concept
- ❏ Exploring The Flight Environment
- ❏ Air Traffic Control System
- ❏ ATC Clearances
- ❏ Interpreting Instrument Charts and Procedures
- ❏ Departure Charts and Procedures
- ❏ Enroute Charts and Procedures
- ❏ Holding Patterns
- ❏ Arrival Charts and Procedures
- ❏ Approach Segments
- ❏ Chart Layout

- ❏ Airport Information
- ❏ Approach Clearance
- ❏ Radar Vectors to Approach
- ❏ Course Reversals
- ❏ Understanding Landing Minimums
- ❏ Inoperative Components
- ❏ Circling and Sidestep Maneuvers
- ❏ Visual and Contact Approaches
- ❏ Various Types of Approaches
- ❏ Evaluating Weather Considerations
- ❏ Examining IFR Flight Considerations
- ❏ IFR Emergencies
- ❏ IFR Decision Making
- ❏ IFR Flight Planning

COMPLETION STANDARDS:

Through oral quizzing, the instructor will determine that the applicant has obtained the necessary instructional knowledge pertaining to learning theories and teaching methods. In addition, the applicant will complete Chapter 6A questions with a minimum passing score of 80 percent and the instructor will review each incorrect response to ensure complete understanding before progressing to Ground Lesson 29.

STUDY ASSIGNMENT:

FLIGHT INSTRUCTOR TEXTBOOK

Chapter 6, Section B — Refining Instrument Skills

STAGE III

GROUND LESSON 29

LESSON REFERENCES:

FLIGHT INSTRUCTOR TEXTBOOK

Chapter 6, Section B — Refining Instrument Skills

GFD FLIGHT INSTRUCTOR VIDEO

Vol V — Instrument Navigation

RECOMMENDED SEQUENCE:

1. Lesson Introduction and Video Presentation
2. Class Discussion

LESSON OBJECTIVES:

During this lesson, the applicant will gain additional knowledge required to teach basic attitude instrument flying. The applicant will learn how to identify common errors, teach students how to cope with instrument failures/partial panel flying, and recover from unusual flight attitudes. The applicant will also improve knowledge and instructional insight regarding instrument navigation, the flight environment, instrument charts and procedures, holding, approach charts and procedures, and weather-related considerations for operations under IFR.

CONTENT:

SECTION B — REFINING INSTRUMENT SKILLS

❑ Preparing for Instrument Instruction
❑ Using PCATDs and FTDs
❑ Flight Planning
❑ Inspecting the Airplane
❑ Developing Instrument Flight Skills
❑ Attitude Instrument Flight
❑ Common Scanning Errors
❑ Using Trim
❑ Getting to Know the Aircraft
❑ Understanding the PTS
❑ Straight-and-Level Flight
❑ Climbs and Descents
❑ Turns to Headings
❑ Practice Patterns
❑ Performing Advanced Instrument Maneuvers
❑ Steep Turns
❑ Vertical S Maneuvers
❑ Stalls
❑ Recovery From Unusual Attitudes
❑ Partial Panel Flying
❑ Mastering Instrument Navigation
❑ VOR Navigation
❑ Distance Measuring Equipment (DME)
❑ ADF Navigation
❑ Area Navigation (RNAV)
❑ Global Positioning System (GPS)
❑ Perfecting Approach Procedures
❑ Radar Approaches
❑ Circling and Sidestep Maneuvers
❑ Missed Approach Procedures

COMPLETION STANDARDS:

The applicant will complete Chapter 6B questions with a minimum passing score of 80 percent and the instructor will review each incorrect response to ensure complete understanding before progressing to ground lesson 30.

STUDY ASSIGNMENT:

Review regulations and related publication pertaining to instrument flight and instrument flight instruction — FAR Parts 61, 91, 141, AIM, PTS, and applicable Advisory Circulars.

STAGE III

GROUND LESSON 30

LESSON REFERENCES:

FAR Parts 61, 91, and 141

Aeronautical Information Manual

Practical Test Standards (Instrument Rating)

FAA-H-8083-15, *Instrument Flying Handbook*

AC 61-65, *Certification: Pilot and Flight Instructors*

RECOMMENDED SEQUENCE:
1. Lesson Introduction
2. Class Discussion

LESSON OBJECTIVES:
During this lesson, the applicant will review and obtain up-to-date instructional knowledge of the requirements for preparing students for an instrument rating. Specifically, the applicant will learn the regulatory knowledge, flight proficiency, and experience requirements, as well as authorized use of flight simulators, flight training devices, or PCATDs. The applicant will also review applicable publications, as required.

CONTENT:

REGULATIONS AND RELATED PUBLICATIONS
❏ FAR Part 61 (Applicable Subparts)
❏ FAR Part 91 (Instrument Flight Rules)
❏ FAR Part 141 (Appendix C)
❏ *Aeronautical Information Manual* (Applicable Subjects)
❏ Practical Test Standards (Instrument Rating)
❏ Logbook Endorsements Related to Instrument Ground and Flight Instruction
❏ Current FAA Advisory Circulars (Applicable Subjects)

COMPLETION STANDARDS:
Through oral quizzing, the instructor will determine that the applicant has obtained the instructional knowledge required to teach the material covered in this lesson before progressing to Ground Lesson 31.

STUDY ASSIGNMENT:
Review format, symbology, terminology, and procedures for departure charts.

STAGE III

GROUND LESSON 31

LESSON REFERENCES:

INSTRUMENT COMMERCIAL TEXTBOOK

Chapter 4, Section A — Departure Charts, and Section B — Departure Procedures

GFD FLIGHT INSTRUCTOR VIDEO

Vol V — Review Departure Procedures

RECOMMENDED SEQUENCE:

1. Lesson Introduction and Audio-visual Presentation
2. Class Discussion

LESSON OBJECTIVES:

During this lesson, the applicant will review and obtain up-to-date instructional knowledge required to teach how to use IFR departure charts, including the associated procedures.

CONTENT:

DEPARTURE CHARTS

❑ Obtaining Charts
❑ *U.S. Standard for Terminal Instrument Procedures* (TERPs)
❑ Climb Gradient
❑ Obstacle Clearance Slope
❑ Instrument Departure Procedure (DP)
❑ Pilot Nav DP
❑ Clearance Procedures
❑ Transitions
❑ Vector DP
❑ Chart Depictions
❑ Textual Descriptions

DEPARTURE PROCEDURES

❑ Departure Options
❑ Takeoff Minimums
❑ VFR Departures
❑ Selecting a Departure Method

COMPLETION STANDARDS:

Through oral quizzing, the instructor will determine that the applicant has obtained the instructional knowledge required to teach the material covered in this lesson before progressing to Ground Lesson 32.

STUDY ASSIGNMENT:

Review format, symbology, terminology, and procedures for Enroute and Area Charts.

STAGE III

GROUND LESSON 32

LESSON REFERENCES:

INSTRUMENT COMMERCIAL TEXTBOOK

Chapter 5, Section A — Enroute and Area Charts, Section B — Enroute Procedures, and Section C — Holding Procedures

GFD FLIGHT INSTRUCTOR VIDEO

Vol V — Review Enroute and Holding Procedures

RECOMMENDED SEQUENCE:

1. Lesson Introduction and Audio-visual Presentation
2. Class Discussion

LESSON OBJECTIVES:

During this lesson, the applicant will obtain up-to-date instructional knowledge required to teach students how to use enroute and area charts, including the pertinent symbology and the associated holding pattern procedures.

CONTENT:

ENROUTE AND AREA CHARTS
- ❑ Enroute Charts
- ❑ Front Panel
- ❑ Navigation Aids
- ❑ Victor Airways
- ❑ Communication
- ❑ Airports
- ❑ Airspace
- ❑ Area Charts

ENROUTE PROCEDURES
- ❑ Enroute Radar Procedures
- ❑ Communication
- ❑ Reporting Procedures
- ❑ Enroute Navigation Using GPS
- ❑ Special Use Airspace
- ❑ IFR Cruising Altitudes
- ❑ Descending From the Enroute Segment

HOLDING PROCEDURES
- ❑ Standard and Nonstandard Pattern
- ❑ Outbound and Inbound Timing
- ❑ Crosswind Correction
- ❑ Maximum Holding Speed
- ❑ Direct Entry
- ❑ Teardrop Entry
- ❑ Parallel Entry
- ❑ Visualizing Entry Procedures
- ❑ ATC Holding Instructions

COMPLETION STANDARDS:
Through oral quizzing, the instructor will determine that the applicant has obtained the instructional knowledge required to teach the material covered in this lesson before progressing to Ground Lesson 33.

STUDY ASSIGNMENT:
Review the *Flight Instructor* textbook, Chapter 6, Sections A and B, the AIM, FAA Regulations and related publications, including the *Instrument/ Commercial* textbook, Chapters 4 and 5 in preparation for the Stage III Exam.

STAGE III

GROUND LESSON 33

STAGE III EXAM

RECOMMENDED SEQUENCE:
1. Lesson Introduction
2. Testing
3. Critique

LESSON OBJECTIVES:
The exam administered during this lesson evaluates the applicant's comprehension of the material presented in Stage III of this course.

CONTENT:
Instrument Flight Instructor Stage III Exam

COMPLETION STANDARDS:
This lesson and stage are complete when the applicant has completed the stage exam with a minimum passing score of 80 percent and the instructor has reviewed each incorrect response to ensure complete understanding before the applicant progresses to Stage IV.

STUDY ASSIGNMENT:
Review arrival charts, arrival procedures, approach charts, and approach procedures.

STAGE IV

STAGE OBJECTIVES

During Stage IV, the applicant will review arrival procedures, VOR, VOR/DME, NDB, LDA, SDF, ILS, GPS approach procedures, and IFR flight planning. The applicant will acquire the instructional knowledge required to teach these subjects including the recognition, analysis, and correction of common student errors.

STAGE COMPLETION STANDARDS

This Stage is complete when the applicant has completed the Stage IV and Flight Instructor—Instrument End-of-Course Exams with a minimum passing score of 80 percent and the instructor has reviewed each incorrect response to ensure complete understanding.

STAGE IV

GROUND LESSON 34

LESSON REFERENCES:

INSTRUMENT COMMERCIAL TEXTBOOK

Chapter 6, Section A — Arrival Charts, Section B — Arrival Procedures, Chapter 7, Section A — Approach Charts, and Section B — Approach Procedures

GFD FLIGHT INSTRUCTOR VIDEO

Vol V — Review Arrival and Approach Procedures

RECOMMENDED SEQUENCE:
1. Lesson Introduction and Audio-visual Presentation
2. Class Discussion

LESSON OBJECTIVES:
During this lesson, the applicant will obtain the instructional knowledge required to teach the correct use of instrument arrival charts and approach charts. The applicant also will learn effective ways to teach the associated arrival and approach procedures.

CONTENT:

ARRIVAL CHARTS AND PROCEDURES
❏ Standard Terminal Arrival Routes
❏ Interpreting the STAR
❏ Vertical Navigation Planning
❏ Preparing for the Arrival
❏ Reviewing the Approach

- ❑ Altitude
- ❑ Airspeed

Approach Charts
- ❑ Initial Approach Segment
- ❑ Intermediate Approach Segment
- ❑ Final Approach Segment
- ❑ Missed Approach Segment
- ❑ Heading Section
- ❑ Plan View
- ❑ Profile View
- ❑ Step Down Fix
- ❑ Landing Minimums
- ❑ Aircraft Approach Categories
- ❑ Minimum Descent Requirements
- ❑ Visibility Requirements
- ❑ Inoperative Components
- ❑ Airport Layout Charts
- ❑ Heading Section
- ❑ Plan View and Additional Runway Information
- ❑ Takeoff and Alternate Minimums

Approach Procedures
- ❑ Preparing for the Approach
- ❑ Approach Chart Review

- ❑ Approach Clearance
- ❑ Executing the Approach
- ❑ Straight-In Approaches
- ❑ Use of ATC Radar for Approaches
- ❑ Approaches Which Require a Course Reversal
- ❑ Timed Approaches From a Holding Fix
- ❑ Final Approach
- ❑ Circling Approaches
- ❑ Sidestep Maneuver
- ❑ Missed Approach Procedures
- ❑ Visual and Contact Approaches

Completion Standards:
Through oral quizzing, the instructor will determine that the applicant has obtained the instructional knowledge required to teach the material covered in this lesson before progressing to Ground Lesson 35.

Study Assignment:
Review instrument approaches — VOR, VOR/DME, NDB, ILS, LDA, SDF, MLS, and GPS/RNAV.

Stage IV

Ground Lesson 35

Lesson References:

Instrument Commercial Textbook

Chapter 8, Section A — VOR and NDB Approaches, Section B — ILS Approaches, and Section C — RNAV Approaches

Recommended Sequence:
1. Lesson Introduction
2. Class Discussion

Lesson Objectives:
During this lesson, the applicant will obtain the instructional knowledge of the essential details related to flying all of the common types of instrument approaches. Specifically, the applicant will learn how to teach the correct procedures for performing VOR, NDB, ILS, LDA, SDF, MLS, and RNAV approaches, including the variations of these instrument procedures.

CONTENT:

VOR AND NDB APPROACHES
- ❑ VOR Approach Procedure
- ❑ Off-Airport Facility
- ❑ On-Airport Facility
- ❑ VOR/DME Procedures
- ❑ NDB Approach Procedure
- ❑ Radar Vectors to the Approach
- ❑ VOR Missed Approach Procedure
- ❑ NDB Missed Approach Procedure

ILS APPROACHES
- ❑ ILS Categories and Minimums
- ❑ ILS Components
- ❑ Inoperative Components
- ❑ Flying the ILS
- ❑ Straight-In (NoPT) ILS Approach
- ❑ ILS Approach with a Course Reversal
- ❑ ILS/DME Approach
- ❑ Radar Vectors to ILS Final
- ❑ ILS Approaches to Parallel Runways
- ❑ Simultaneous Converging Instrument Approach
- ❑ Localizer Approach
- ❑ Localizer Back Course Approach
- ❑ LDA, SDF, and MLS Approaches

RNAV APPROACHES
- ❑ Lateral Navigation
- ❑ Vertical Navigation
- ❑ GPS Equipment Requirements
- ❑ The Navigation Database
- ❑ Special GPS Navigation Considerations
- ❑ GPS Overlay Approach
- ❑ GPS Stand Alone Approach
- ❑ Radar Vectors to a GPS Approach
- ❑ VOR/DME RNAV

COMPLETION STANDARDS:
Through oral quizzing, the instructor will determine that the applicant has obtained the instructional knowledge required to teach the material covered in this lesson before progressing to Ground Lesson 36.

STUDY ASSIGNMENT:
Review meteorology, including weather factors, hazards, printed reports and forecasts, sources of weather information, in-flight weather sources, and airborne weather equipment.

STAGE IV

GROUND LESSON 36

LESSON REFERENCES:

INSTRUMENT COMMERCIAL TEXTBOOK

Chapter 9 — Meteorology

RECOMMENDED SEQUENCE:
1. Lesson Introduction
2. Class Discussion

LESSON OBJECTIVES:
During this lesson, the applicant will obtain the instructional knowledge of weather information. Specifically, the applicant will learn about procurement and use of aviation weather reports and

forecasts and the elements of forecasting weather trends based on that information and personal observation of weather conditions. The applicant also will review procedures for safe and efficient operation of aircraft under instrument flight rules and conditions, and recognition of critical weather situations and wind shear avoidance.

CONTENT:

METEOROLOGY
❏ Weather Factors
❏ Weather Hazards
❏ Printed Reports and Forecasts
❏ Graphic weather Products

❏ Sources of Weather Information
❏ In-Flight Weather Sources
❏ Airborne Weather Equipment

COMPLETION STANDARDS:
Through oral quizzing, the instructor will determine that the applicant has obtained the instructional knowledge required to teach the material covered in this lesson before progressing to Ground Lesson 37.

STUDY ASSIGNMENT:
Review IFR flight considerations, including IFR emergencies, IFR decision making, and IFR flight planning.

STAGE IV

GROUND
LESSON 37

LESSON REFERENCES:

INSTRUMENT COMMERCIAL
TEXTBOOK

Chapter 10, IFR Flight Considerations

RECOMMENDED SEQUENCE:
1. Lesson Introduction
2. Class Discussion

LESSON OBJECTIVES:
During this lesson, the applicant will obtain the instructional knowledge of IFR emergency procedures and decision making. Specifically, the applicant will gain additional insight into aeronautical decision making and

judgment, as well as crew resource management, including crew communication and coordination. The applicant will also learn how to teach these subjects, along with IFR flight planning.

CONTENT:

IFR EMERGENCIES
❏ Declaring an Emergency
❏ Minimum Fuel
❏ Gyroscopic Instrument Failure
❏ Emergency Approach Procedures
❏ Malfunction Reports

IFR DECISION MAKING
❏ Decision-Making Process
❏ IFR Accident
❏ Poor Judgment Chain
❏ Assessing Risk
❏ Pilot-In-Command Responsibility
❏ Hazardous Attitudes
❏ Crew Relationships
❏ Communication
❏ Resource Use
❏ Workload Management
❏ Situational Awareness

IFR Flight Planning
- ❏ Route Selection
- ❏ Flight Information Publications
- ❏ Weather Considerations
- ❏ Altitude Selection
- ❏ Completing the Navigation Log
- ❏ Filing the Flight Plan
- ❏ Closing the IFR Flight Plan

Completion Standards:
Through oral quizzing, the instructor will determine that the applicant has obtained the instructional knowledge required to teach the material covered in this lesson before progressing to Ground Lesson 38.

Study Assignment:
Complete preparation for the Instrument Flight Instructor Oral Questions Briefing and the Stage IV Exam.

Stage IV

Ground Lesson 38

Pilot Briefing and Stage IV Exam

Lesson References:

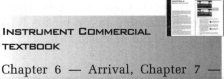

Instrument Commercial textbook

Chapter 6 — Arrival, Chapter 7 — Approach, Chapter 8 — Instrument Approaches, Chapter 9 — Meteorology, and Chapter 10 — IFR Flight Considerations

Recommended Sequence:
1. Lesson Introduction
2. Class Discussion
3. Testing
4. Critique

Lesson Objectives:
Prior to this lesson, the applicant will prepare answers to the essay questions contained in the Instrument Flight Instructor Oral Questions Pilot Briefing using appropriate references. During the discussion, the applicant will explain the answers given and demonstrate that the material is thoroughly understood. The applicant will demonstrate the ability to apply this knowledge to instrument flight instruction. The exam administered during this lesson evaluates student comprehension of the material in Stage IV.

Content:
- ❏ Instrument Flight Instructor Oral Questions
- ❏ Attitude Instrument Flying
- ❏ Instrument Charts
- ❏ Instrument Approach Procedures
- ❏ IFR Emergency Procedures
- ❏ General Subjects
- ❏ Stage IV Exam

Completion Standards:
The applicant will demonstrate that each question in the Pilot Briefing is completely understood and the information can be clearly conveyed to a student. This lesson and stage are complete when the student has completed

the Stage IV Exam with a minimum passing score of 80 percent. The instructor will review each incorrect response to ensure complete understanding.

STUDY ASSIGNMENT:
The applicant should review the *Flight Instructor* textbook, as necessary. In addition, the applicant may review appropriate information in the *Instrument/commercial* textbook, as required, in preparation for the Flight Instructor — Instrument End-of-Course Exam.

STAGE IV

GROUND LESSON 39

Flight Instructor — Instrument End-of-Course Exam

RECOMMENDED SEQUENCE:
1. Lesson Introduction
2. Testing
3. Critique

LESSON OBJECTIVES:
This testing session evaluates the applicant's comprehension of the material presented in Stages III and IV in preparation for the FAA Flight Instructor-Instrument Airmen Knowledge Test.

CONTENT:
Flight Instructor — Instrument End-of-Course Examination.

COMPLETION STANDARDS:
The applicant will complete the Flight Instructor — Instrument End-of-Course Exam with a minimum passing score of 80 percent and the instructor will review each incorrect response to ensure complete understanding.

STUDY ASSIGNMENT:
As recommended by the flight instructor in preparation for the FAA knowledge and practical tests.

INSTRUMENT INSTRUCTOR FLIGHT TRAINING SYLLABUS
STAGE III

STAGE OBJECTIVES

During this stage, the applicant will learn the analysis and performance of the maneuvers and procedures required for an instrument rating, airplane from the right seat of the training airplane, including appropriate safety of flight practices.

STAGE COMPLETION STANDARDS

The applicant must successfully complete each of the lessons in Stage III and demonstrate appropriate crew resource management and collision avoidance precautions, including the positive exchange of aircraft control when necessary. Additionally, the applicant will be able to analyze and perform all the maneuvers and procedures from the right seat of the training airplane in accordance with the criteria set forth in the current FAA instrument rating and flight instructor, instrument practical test standards, as appropriate.

STAGE III

FLIGHT LESSON 18

DUAL

LESSON OBJECTIVES:

During this lesson, the applicant is introduced to the performance of attitude instrument maneuvers while flying from the right seat of the training airplane. In addition, the applicant will learn to analyze and perform the elements of the listed maneuvers. The applicant also will explain the importance of maintaining situational awareness to prevent runway incursion incidents in instrument conditions.

CONTENT:

LESSON INTRODUCTION

PREFLIGHT PREPARATION
❏ Weather Information
❏ Cross-Country Flight Planning
❏ Use of Checklists
❏ Instrument Cockpit Check
❏ Crew Resource Management
❏ Positive Exchange of Controls

AIRPORT OPERATIONS
❏ Airport, Runway, and Taxiway Signs, Markings, and Lighting
❏ Collision Avoidance Precautions
❏ Runway Incursion Avoidance
   ❏ Use of aircraft lighting during taxi and takeoff operations.
   ❏ Readback/hearback on
     (1) Hold Short,
     (2) Position and Hold, and
     (3) Runway Crossings.
❏ Land and Hold Short Operations (LAHSO)

AIRCRAFT SYSTEMS RELATED TO IFR OPERATIONS
❑ Aircraft Anti-Icing
❑ Aircraft Deicing

ATTITUDE INSTRUMENT FLYING
❑ Fundamentals of Attitude Instrument Flying
❑ Pitch Control
❑ Bank Control
❑ Power Control

FLIGHT BY REFERENCE TO INSTRUMENTS
❑ Straight-and-Level Flight
❑ Turns
❑ Change of Airspeed in Straight-and-Level and Turning Flight
❑ Constant Airspeed Climbs and Descents
❑ Constant Rate Climbs and Descents
❑ Timed Turns to Magnetic Compass Headings
❑ Steep Turns
❑ Recovery from Unusual Flight Attitudes

POSTFLIGHT PROCEDURES
❑ Engine Shutdown
❑ Securing the Aircraft
❑ Checking Instruments and Equipment

COMPLETION STANDARDS:
At the completion of this lesson, the applicant will be able to perform and analyze the procedures for basic attitude instrument flying. During the performance of all maneuvers, both full and partial panel, altitude will be maintained within 100 feet, heading within 10°, and airspeed within 10 knots of that assigned. Recoveries from unusual flight attitudes will be smooth and accurately executed within the operating limitations of the airplane.

POSTFLIGHT DISCUSSION AND PREVIEW OF NEXT LESSON

LESSON ASSIGNMENT:
Ground Lesson 29

STAGE III

FLIGHT LESSON 19

DUAL

LESSON OBJECTIVES:
During this lesson, the applicant will develop the ability to demonstrate accurate instrument navigation and compliance with air traffic control clearances and procedures. The applicant will learn to correctly analyze and perform the elements of each maneuver or procedure listed for review. The applicant will discuss how the use of checklists is an essential element of effective resource use and workload management.

CONTENT:

LESSON REVIEW

PREFLIGHT PREPARATION
❑ Weather Information
❑ Cross-Country Flight Planning

AIRPORT OPERATIONS
❑ Airport, Runway, and Taxiway Signs, Markings, and Lighting
❑ Collision Avoidance Precautions

❑ Runway Incursion Avoidance/ LAHSO

AIRCRAFT SYSTEMS RELATED TO IFR OPERATIONS
❑ Aircraft Anti-Icing
❑ Aircraft Deicing

ATTITUDE INSTRUMENT FLYING
❑ Fundamentals of Attitude Instrument Flying
❑ Pitch Control
❑ Bank Control
❑ Power Control

FLIGHT BY REFERENCE TO INSTRUMENTS
❑ Straight-and-Level Flight
❑ Turns
❑ Change of Airspeed in Straight-and-Level and Turning Flight
❑ Constant Airspeed Climbs and Descents
❑ Constant Rate Climbs and Descents
❑ Timed Turns to Magnetic Compass Headings
❑ Steep Turns
❑ Recovery from Unusual Flight Attitudes

LESSON INTRODUCTION

AIR TRAFFIC CONTROL CLEARANCES AND PROCEDURES
❑ Air Traffic Control Clearances
❑ Compliance with Departure, Enroute, and Arrival Procedures and Clearances

NAVIGATION AIDS
❑ Intercepting and Tracking Navigational Systems and DME Arcs
❑ Holding Procedures

COMPLETION STANDARDS:
At the completion of this lesson, the applicant will be able to demonstrate the correct procedures for instrument navigation. The applicant will perform all the maneuvers correctly and accurately while maintaining constant orientation. The applicant will promptly and correctly comply with all ATC instructions and clearances. In addition, the applicant will be able to analyze and perform the important elements of full and partial panel basic instrument maneuvers.

POSTFLIGHT DISCUSSION AND PREVIEW OF NEXT LESSON

LESSON ASSIGNMENT:
Ground Lesson 30

STAGE III
FLIGHT LESSON 20

DUAL

LESSON OBJECTIVES:
During this lesson, the applicant will develop the ability to perform holding patterns, non-precision approaches, and lost communications and navigation equipment procedures. In addition, the applicant will learn the analysis and performance of air traffic control clearances and procedures and tracking navigational systems and DME arcs. The applicant also will discuss the importance of maintaining situational awareness and position orientation when navigating in the IFR environment.

CONTENT:
LESSON REVIEW
AIR TRAFFIC CONTROL CLEARANCES AND PROCEDURES
❏ Air Traffic Control Clearances
❏ Compliance with Departure, Enroute, and Arrival Procedures and Clearances

NAVIGATION AIDS
❏ Intercepting and Tracking Navigational Systems and DME Arcs
❏ Holding Procedures

LESSON INTRODUCTION
HOLDING PROCEDURES
❏ Standard and Non-Standard Patterns
❏ Published and Nonpublished Patterns
❏ DME Holding
❏ Holding at Navigation Aids
❏ Intersection Holding

INSTRUMENT APPROACH PROCEDURES
❏ Non-Precision Instrument Approach
❏ Missed Approach
❏ Circling Approach
❏ Landing from a Straight-In Approach

EMERGENCY OPERATIONS
❏ Systems and Equipment Malfunctions
❏ Loss of Radio Communications
❏ Loss of Navigation Equipment
❏ Loss of Gyro Attitude and Heading Indicators
❏ Emergency Equipment and Survival Gear

AERONAUTICAL DECISION MAKING AND JUDGMENT

COMPLETION STANDARDS:
At the completion of this lesson, the applicant will be able to demonstrate the proper procedures for holding patterns and non-precision instrument approaches. Instrument navigation will be demonstrated correctly and accurately, while maintaining constant orientation. During the review portion of the lesson, the applicant will demonstrate the correct analysis and performance of air traffic control clearances and procedures and tracking navigational systems and DME arcs.

POSTFLIGHT DISCUSSION AND PREVIEW OF NEXT LESSON

LESSON ASSIGNMENT:
Ground Lesson 31

STAGE III

FLIGHT LESSON 21

DUAL

LESSON OBJECTIVES:
During this lesson, the applicant will learn the correct performance of localizer and ILS/RNAV approaches and the technique used for circling approaches and landings from straight-in and circling approaches. The applicant will develop the ability to correctly analyze and perform holding pattern procedures, non-precision approaches, and missed approaches. In addition, the applicant will demonstrate effective resource use, proper communication skills, and workload management skills.

CONTENT:

LESSON REVIEW

STANDARD AND NON-STANDARD PATTERNS
❑ Published and Nonpublished Patterns
❑ DME Holding
❑ Holding at Navaids
❑ Intersection Holding

INSTRUMENT APPROACH PROCEDURES
❑ VOR/VORTAC Instrument Approach Procedures (if so equipped)
❑ NDB Instrument Approach Procedures (if so equipped)
❑ Missed Approach Procedures

EMERGENCY OPERATIONS

AERONAUTICAL DECISION MAKING AND JUDGMENT

LESSON INTRODUCTION

INSTRUMENT APPROACH PROCEDURES
❑ Localizer Instrument Approach Procedures Including Back Course
❑ ILS Instrument Approach Procedures
❑ RNAV Approach (if so equipped)
❑ Circling Approach Procedures
❑ Landing from Straight-in and Circling Approaches
❑ Partial Panel Non-precision Approach

COMPLETION STANDARDS:
At the completion of this lesson, the applicant will be able to perform non-precision approaches in accordance with the FAA instrument rating practical test standards. Missed approaches will be performed as outlined on the approach chart. The applicant will be able to correctly analyze and perform holding patterns and lost communications and navigation procedures.

POSTFLIGHT DISCUSSION AND PREVIEW OF NEXT LESSON

LESSON ASSIGNMENT:
Ground Lessons 32 and 33

STAGE III

FLIGHT LESSON 22

DUAL

LESSON OBJECTIVES:
During this lesson, the applicant will learn to analyze and perform the instrument approach procedures listed for review. In addition, the applicant will exhibit sound ADM and judgment skills.

CONTENT:

LESSON REVIEW

INSTRUMENT APPROACH PROCEDURES
❏ Localizer Instrument Approach Procedures Including Back Course
❏ ILS/RNAV Instrument Approach Procedures

❏ Circling Approach Procedures
❏ Landing from Straight-in and Circling Approaches
❏ Missed Approach Procedures
❏ Partial Panel Non-precision Approach

COMPLETION STANDARDS:
At the completion of this lesson, the applicant will be able to analyze and perform the approaches and approach procedures listed for review. Each of the approaches and approach procedures will be performed in accordance with the current FAA instrument rating practical test standards.

POSTFLIGHT DISCUSSION AND PREVIEW OF NEXT LESSON

LESSON ASSIGNMENT:
Ground Lesson 34

STAGE III

FLIGHT LESSON 23

DUAL

STAGE CHECK

RECOMMENDED SEQUENCE:
1. Preflight Orientation
2. Flight
3. Postflight Evaluation

LESSON OBJECTIVES:
This lesson is a stage check, conducted by the chief flight instructor, assistant chief instructor, or a designated assistant, to evaluate the applicant's ability to correctly analyze and safely perform the listed maneuvers or procedures. In addition, the applicant will describe relevant ADM principles, including pilot-in-command responsibility.

CONTENT:

LESSON REVIEW

PREFLIGHT PREPARATION

ATTITUDE INSTRUMENT FLYING

FLIGHT BY REFERENCE TO INSTRUMENTS

❏ Straight-and-Level Flight
❏ Turns
❏ Change of Airspeed in Straight-and-Level and Turning Flight
❏ Constant Airspeed Climbs and Descents
❏ Constant Rate Climbs and Descents
❏ Timed Turns to Magnetic Compass Headings
❏ Steep Turns
❏ Recovery from Unusual Flight Attitudes

AIR TRAFFIC CONTROL CLEARANCES AND PROCEDURES

INTERCEPTING AND TRACKING NAVIGATIONAL SYSTEMS AND DME ARCS

HOLDING PROCEDURES

EMERGENCY OPERATIONS

INSTRUMENT APPROACH PROCEDURES

COMPLETION STANDARDS:

At the completion of this lesson, the applicant will safely demonstrate the performance of each of the listed maneuvers and procedures at a proficiency level that meets or exceeds that outlined in the current FAA instrument rating practical test standards. The applicant will be able to correctly analyze the elements associated with the performance of each maneuver and procedure.

POSTFLIGHT DISCUSSION AND PREVIEW OF NEXT LESSON

LESSON ASSIGNMENT:

Ground Lesson 34

STAGE IV

STAGE OBJECTIVES

During this stage of instruction, the applicant will acquire the instructional knowledge of the elements of each of the listed maneuvers and procedures including the recognition, analysis, and correction of common student errors. The applicant will be able to prepare a lesson plan for each flight and be able to safely conduct the flight according to the planned lesson, including effective preflight and postflight instruction.

STAGE COMPLETION STANDARDS

The applicant will successfully and safely complete each of the flight lessons in Stage IV. At the completion of the stage, the applicant will have the proficiency and instructional knowledge of a competent instrument flight instructor with an airplane, single-engine class rating. The proficiency level will meet or exceed the criteria of the current FAA instrument rating and flight instructor, instrument practical test standards.

STAGE IV

FLIGHT LESSON 24

DUAL

LESSON OBJECTIVES:

During this lesson, the applicant will obtain the instructional knowledge of the elements of preflight preparation, ground operations, attitude instrument flying, and full and partial panel basic instrument maneuvers. This will include the recognition, analysis, and correction of common errors. In addition, the applicant will include relevant ADM principles in the lesson.

CONTENT:

LESSON INTRODUCTION

PREFLIGHT PREPARATION

❑ Weather Information
❑ Cross-Country Flight Planning
❑ Use of Checklists
❑ Instrument Cockpit Check
❑ Positive Exchange of Flight Controls

AIRCRAFT SYSTEMS RELATED TO IFR OPERATIONS

❑ Aircraft Anti-Icing
❑ Aircraft Deicing

ATTITUDE INSTRUMENT FLYING

❑ Fundamentals of Attitude Instrument Flying
❑ Pitch Control
❑ Bank Control
❑ Power Control

FLIGHT BY REFERENCE TO INSTRUMENTS

❑ Straight-and-Level Flight
❑ Turns

- Change of Airspeed in Straight-and-Level and Turning Flight
- Constant Airspeed Climbs and Descents
- Constant Rate Climbs and Descents
- Timed Turns to Magnetic Compass Headings
- Steep Turns
- Recovery from Unusual Flight Attitudes

COMPLETION STANDARDS:

At the completion of this lesson, the applicant will be able to analyze and perform each of the listed maneuvers and procedures at the competency level that meets or exceeds the criteria outlined in the current FAA instrument rating and flight instructor, instrument practical test standards. In addition, the applicant will demonstrate the instructional knowledge of the elements of the maneuver or procedure, including the recognition, analysis, and correction of common student errors.

POSTFLIGHT DISCUSSION AND PREVIEW OF NEXT LESSON

LESSON ASSIGNMENT:

Ground Lesson 35

STAGE IV

FLIGHT LESSON 25

DUAL

LESSON OBJECTIVES:

During this lesson, the applicant will practice the review maneuvers and procedures to further develop instructional techniques. In addition, the applicant will begin to obtain the instructional knowledge of the elements of air traffic control clearances and procedures and the use of navigational aids, including recognition analysis, and correction of common student errors. The applicant also will demonstrate the ability to incorporate ADM principles into instrument flight lessons. For example, the use of checklists can be emphasized as an important resource used to enhance a student's ability to manage workload.

CONTENT:

LESSON REVIEW

PREFLIGHT PREPARATION
- Weather Information
- Cross-Country Flight Planning
- Use of Checklists
- Instrument Cockpit Check

AIRCRAFT SYSTEMS RELATED TO IFR OPERATIONS
- Aircraft Anti-Icing
- Aircraft Deicing

ATTITUDE INSTRUMENT FLYING
- Fundamentals of Attitude Instrument Flying
- Pitch Control

- ❏ Bank Control
- ❏ Power Control

FLIGHT BY REFERENCE TO INSTRUMENTS

- ❏ Straight-and-Level Flight
- ❏ Turns
- ❏ Change of Airspeed in Straight-and-Level and Turning Flight
- ❏ Constant Airspeed Climbs and Descents
- ❏ Constant Rate Climbs and Descents
- ❏ Timed Turns to Magnetic Compass Headings
- ❏ Steep Turns
- ❏ Recovery from Unusual Flight Attitudes

LESSON INTRODUCTION

AIR TRAFFIC CONTROL CLEARANCES AND PROCEDURES

- ❏ Air Traffic Control Clearances
- ❏ Compliance with Departure, Enroute, and Arrival Procedures and Clearances

NAVIGATION AIDS

- ❏ Intercepting and Tracking Navigational Systems and DME Arcs
- ❏ Time/Speed/Distance Computations

COMPLETION STANDARDS:

At the completion of this lesson, the applicant will be able to analyze and perform each of the listed maneuvers and procedures at a competency level that meets or exceeds the criteria outlined in the current FAA instrument rating and flight instructor, instrument practical test standards. In addition, the applicant will demonstrate the instructional knowledge of the elements of the maneuvers and procedures listed for review, including analysis, recognition, and correction of common student errors of the maneuvers listed for review.

POSTFLIGHT DISCUSSION AND PREVIEW OF NEXT LESSON

LESSON ASSIGNMENT:

Ground Lesson 36

STAGE IV

FLIGHT LESSON 26

DUAL

LESSON OBJECTIVES:

During this lesson, the applicant will practice the review maneuvers and procedures to further develop instructional techniques. In addition, the applicant will begin to obtain the instructional knowledge of the elements of holding pattern procedures,

loss of communications and navigation equipment, non-precision instrument approaches, and missed approaches including recognition, analysis, and correction of common student errors. The applicant will apply ADM principles to the lesson, including how students can recognize hazardous attitudes.

CONTENT:

LESSON REVIEW

Air Traffic Control Clearances and Procedures

- ❑ Air Traffic Control Clearances
- ❑ Compliance with Departure, Enroute, and Arrival Procedures and Clearances

Navigation Aids

- ❑ Intercepting and Tracking Navigational Systems and DME Arcs
- ❑ Time/Speed/Distance Computations

Lesson Introduction

Holding Procedures

- ❑ Standard and Nonstandard Patterns
- ❑ Published and Nonpublished Patterns
- ❑ DME Holding
- ❑ Holding at Navaids
- ❑ Intersection Holding

Instrument Approach Procedures

- ❑ Non-Precision Instrument Approach Procedures
- ❑ Missed Approach Procedures

Emergency Operations

- ❑ Systems and Equipment Malfunctions

- ❑ Loss of Radio Communications
- ❑ Loss of Navigational Equipment
- ❑ Loss of Gyro Attitude and Heading Indicators
- ❑ Emergency Equipment and Survival Gear

Completion Standards:

At the completion of this lesson, the applicant will be able to analyze and perform each of the listed maneuvers and procedures at a competency level that meets or exceeds the criteria outlined in the current FAA instrument rating and flight instructor, instrument practical test standards. In addition, the applicant will demonstrate the instructional knowledge of the elements of the maneuvers and procedures listed for review, including recognition, analysis, and correction of common student errors.

Postflight Discussion and Preview of Next Lesson

Lesson Assignment:

Ground Lesson 37

Stage IV

Flight Lesson 27

Dual

Lesson Objectives:

During this lesson, the applicant will practice the review maneuvers and procedures to further develop instructional techniques. In addition, the applicant will begin to obtain the instructional knowledge of the elements of localizer and ILS/GPS instrument approaches, circling approach procedures, and landings from straight-in and circling approaches, including recognition, analysis, and correction of common student errors. The applicant will apply ADM principles to the lesson, including how students can avoid common operational pitfalls during holding patterns and approaches.

CONTENT:

LESSON REVIEW

HOLDING PROCEDURES
❏ Standard and Nonstandard Patterns
❏ Published and Nonpublished Patterns
❏ DME Holding
❏ Holding at Navaids
❏ Intersection Holding

INSTRUMENT APPROACH PROCEDURES
❏ Non-Precision Instrument Approach Procedures
❏ Missed Approach Procedures

EMERGENCY OPERATIONS

LESSON INTRODUCTION

INSTRUMENT APPROACH PROCEDURES
❏ Localizer Instrument Approach Procedures, including Back Course
❏ ILS Instrument Approach Procedures
❏ Circling Approach Procedures
❏ Landing from Straight-in and Circling Approaches

❏ Missed Approach Procedures
❏ Partial Panel Non-precision Approach

COMPLETION STANDARDS:
At the completion of this lesson, the applicant will be able to analyze and perform each of the listed maneuvers and procedures at a competency level that meets or exceeds the criteria outlined in the current FAA instrument rating and flight instructor, instrument practical test standards. In addition, the applicant will demonstrate the instructional knowledge of the elements of the maneuvers and procedures listed for review, including recognition, analysis, and correction of common student errors.

POSTFLIGHT DISCUSSION AND PREVIEW OF NEXT LESSON

LESSON ASSIGNMENT:
Ground Lesson 38

STAGE IV

FLIGHT LESSON 28

DUAL

LESSON OBJECTIVES:
During this lesson, the applicant will obtain the instructional knowledge of the elements of localizer and ILS/GPS instrument approaches, circling approach procedures, and landings from straight-in and circling approaches, including recognition, analysis, and correction of common student errors. The applicant will conduct the flight in the role of flight instructor, demonstrating and evaluating the performance of each maneuver. The applicant will describe the relevance of using good workload management techniques during instrument approaches and demonstrate an understanding of CFIT.

CONTENT:

LESSON REVIEW

INSTRUMENT APPROACH PROCEDURES
❑ Non-Precision Instrument Approach
❑ Precision Instrument Approach
❑ Missed Approach
❑ Circling Approach
❑ Landing from a Straight-In Approach

COMPLETION STANDARDS:
At the completion of this lesson, the applicant will be able to analyze and perform each of the listed maneuvers and procedures at a competency level that meets or exceeds the criteria outlined in the current FAA instrument rating and flight instructor, instrument practical test standards. In addition, the applicant will demonstrate the instructional knowledge of the elements of the maneuvers and procedures, including recognition, analysis, and correction of common student errors.

POSTFLIGHT DISCUSSION AND PREVIEW OF NEXT LESSON

LESSON ASSIGNMENT:
Ground Lesson 39

STAGE IV

FLIGHT LESSON 29

DUAL

STAGE CHECK

LESSON OBJECTIVES:
During this lesson, the chief instructor, assistant chief instructor, or a designated check instructor will determine that the applicant safely and efficiently meets the proficiency requirements for an instrument flight instructor with an airplane, single-engine class rating. In addition, the applicant's ability to apply the ADM principles of pilot-in-command responsibility, communication, workload management, resource use and situational awareness to ground and flight operations will be evaluated.

CONTENT:

LESSON REVIEW

PREFLIGHT PREPARATION

PREFLIGHT LESSON ON A MANEUVER TO BE PERFORMED FLIGHT
❑ Maneuver Lesson

FLIGHT BY REFERENCE TO INSTRUMENTS
❑ Straight-and-Level Flight
❑ Turns
❑ Change of Airspeed in Straight-and-Level and Turning Flight
❑ Constant Airspeed Climbs and Descents
❑ Constant Rate Climbs and Descents

- ❏ Timed Turns to Magnetic Compass Headings
- ❏ Steep Turns
- ❏ Recovery from Unusual Flight Attitudes

AIR TRAFFIC CONTROL CLEARANCES AND PROCEDURES

INTERCEPTING AND TRACKING NAVIGATIONAL SYSTEMS AND DME ARCS

HOLDING PROCEDURES

EMERGENCY OPERATIONS

INSTRUMENT APPROACH PROCEDURES

AERONAUTICAL DECISION MAKING AND JUDGMENT

COMPLETION STANDARDS:
At the completion of this lesson, the applicant will demonstrate the skill and instructional knowledge required to successfully and safely complete the flight instructor, instrument practical test. Each maneuver and procedure will be performed at a proficiency level that meets or exceeds the criteria outlined in the current FAA instrument rating and flight instructor, instrument practical test standards.

POSTFLIGHT DISCUSSION

STAGE IV

FLIGHT LESSON 30

DUAL — END-OF-COURSE FLIGHT CHECK

LESSON OBJECTIVE
During this lesson, the chief instructor, assistant chief instructor, or a designated check instructor will determine that the applicant meets the knowledge and proficiency requirements for a an instrument flight instructor with an airplane, single-engine class rating.

NOTE: *End-of-course flight checks include a broad range of knowledge and skill areas listed in the Flight Instructor Practical Test Standards (PTS). However, since it is impractical to complete all of the listed tasks on one flight check, the end-of-course checks should be conducted as a practical test. According to the practical test concept, an examiner may select specific tasks within an area of operation for testing purposes. Some areas of operation contain tasks that require the applicant to demonstrate instructional knowledge, others specify proficiency or demonstration of skill, and in some cases, certain tasks must be evaluated. All instructors and instructor applicants should be familiar with the practical test concept.*

CONTENT:

LESSON REVIEW

FUNDAMENTALS OF INSTRUCTING

❑ The Learning Process
❑ Human Behavior and Effective Communication
❑ The Teaching Process
❑ Teaching Methods
❑ Critique and Evaluation
❑ Flight Instructor Characteristics and Responsibilities
❑ Planning Instructional Activity

TECHNICAL SUBJECT AREAS

❑ Aircraft Flight Instruments and Navigation Equipment
❑ Aeromedical Factors
❑ Federal Aviation Regulations Related to IFR Operations
❑ Publications Related to Instrument Flight and Instrument Flight Instruction
❑ Logbook Entries Related to Instrument Instruction

PREFLIGHT PREPARATION

❑ Obtaining Weather Information
❑ Cross-Country Flight Planning
❑ Instrument Cockpit Check

PREFLIGHT LESSON ON A MANEUVER TO BE PERFORMED IN FLIGHT

❑ Maneuver Lesson

AIR TRAFFIC CONTROL CLEARANCES AND PROCEDURES

❑ Air Traffic Control Clearances
❑ Compliance with Departure, Enroute, and Arrival Procedures and Clearances

FLIGHT BY REFERENCE TO INSTRUMENTS

❑ Straight-and-Level Flight
❑ Turns
❑ Change of Airspeed in Straight-and-Level and Turning Flight
❑ Constant Airspeed Climbs and Descents
❑ Constant Rate Climbs and Descents
❑ Timed Turns to Magnetic Compass Headings
❑ Steep Turns
❑ Recovery from Unusual Flight Attitudes

NAVIGATION AIDS

❑ Intercepting and Tracking Navigational Systems and DME Arcs
❑ Holding Procedures

INSTRUMENT APPROACH PROCEDURES

❑ Non-Precision Instrument Approach
❑ Precision Instrument Approach
❑ Missed Approach
❑ Circling Approach
❑ Landing from a Straight-In Approach

EMERGENCY OPERATIONS

❑ Loss of Communications
❑ Loss of Gyro Attitude and Heading Indicators
❑ Engine Failure During Straight-and-Level Flight and Turns

POSTFLIGHT PROCEDURES

❑ Checking Instruments and Equipment

AERONAUTICAL DECISION MAKING AND JUDGMENT

COMPLETION STANDARDS:

At the completion of this lesson, the applicant will demonstrate satisfactory performance according to the appropriate FAA practical test standards with regard to:

1. knowledge of the fundamentals of instructing;
2. knowledge of the technical subject areas;
3. knowledge of the flight instructor's responsibilities concerning the pilot certification process;
4. knowledge of the flight instructor's responsibilities concerning logbook entries and pilot certificate endorsements;
5. ability to demonstrate the procedures and maneuvers selected by the examiner to at least the instrument pilot skill level while giving effective instruction;
6. competence in teaching the procedures and maneuvers selected by the examiner;
7. competence in describing, recognizing, analyzing, and correcting common errors simulated by the examiner; and
8. knowledge of the development and effective use of a course of training, a syllabus, and a lesson plan.

POSTFLIGHT DISCUSSION

Multi-Engine Flight Instructor Certification Course

Course Objectives
The applicant will obtain the knowledge, skill, and aeronautical experience necessary to meet the requirements for the addition of a multi-engine, airplane class rating to an existing flight instructor certificate.

Course Completion Standards
The applicant will demonstrate through written tests and flight tests, and show through appropriate records, that the knowledge, skill, and experience requirements necessary for the addition of a multi-engine, airplane class rating to an existing flight instructor certificate have been obtained.

Ground Training Course Objectives
The applicant will obtain the necessary aeronautical knowledge, instructional background, and meet the prerequisites specified in Part 61 to effectively teach in multi-engine airplanes.

Completion Standards
The applicant will demonstrate, through oral tests, written tests, and records, that the prerequisites specified in Part 61 have been met and the necessary knowledge to effectively teach in a multi-engine airplane has been obtained.

Flight Training Course Objectives
The applicant will obtain the aeronautical skill, instructional knowledge, and experience necessary to meet the requirements for the addition of a multi-engine, airplane class rating to an existing flight instructor certificate.

Completion Standards
The applicant will demonstrate, through flight tests and school records, that the aeronautical skill, instructional knowledge, and experience necessary to meet the requirements for the addition of a multi-engine, airplane class rating to an existing flight instructor certificate have been obtained.

MULTI-ENGINE FLIGHT INSTRUCTOR CERTIFICATION COURSE OVERVIEW

MULTI-ENGINE FLIGHT INSTRUCTOR CERTIFICATION COURSE

The following time analysis indicates compliance with Part 141, Appendix F.

MINIMUM COURSE HOURS

	GROUND TRAINING				FLIGHT TRAINING			
	Briefing Sessions	AV and Class Discussion	Stage / End-of-Course Exams	Exam Debriefings	Maneuver Analysis	Practice Instruction	Stage/ End-of-Course Checks	Preflight/ Postflight Briefings
Stage V		8.0	.5	As Req.	12.0		1.5	As Req.
Stage VI	2.0	6.0	2.5	1.0		13.0	3.5	As Req.
TOTAL	2.0	14.0	3.0	1.0	12.0	13.0	5.0	As Req.

Note: *The times for stage and end-of-course checks are included in the totals for maneuver analysis and practice instruction.*

APPLICANT INFORMATION

COURSE ENROLLMENT

To enroll in the multi-engine flight instructor course, you must have a commercial pilot certificate or an airline transport pilot certificate, with a category, class, and instrument rating appropriate to the aircraft category and class rating for which the course applies. In addition, you must hold a flight instructor certificate with an airplane category rating and a single-engine class rating.

REQUIREMENTS FOR GRADUATION

To obtain a multi-engine flight instructor rating, you must successfully complete all of the ground and Flight Lessons contained in Stages V and VI. In addition, you must have at least 15 hours of pilot-in-command experience in multi-engine land airplanes at the completion of the course.

LESSON DESCRIPTION AND STAGES OF TRAINING

Each lesson is fully described within the syllabus, including the objectives, standards, and measurable units of accomplishment and learning for each lesson. The objectives and standards of each stage are described within the syllabus.

TESTS AND CHECKS

The syllabus incorporates stage checks in accordance with Part 141. These checks are given by the chief instructor, the assistant chief instructor, or a designated check instructor at the end of each stage. You also will complete the appropriate stage exams, pilot briefings, and end of course examinations that are described within the syllabus. In addition, you must satisfactorily accomplish an end-of-course test after all of the stages have been completed.

LESSON TIME ALLOCATION

Pilot Briefings	AV Presentation & Class Discussion	Stage & End-Of-Course Exam Completion	Stage & End-of-Course Exam Debriefing		Maneuver Analysis	Practice Instruction	Stage/E-O-C Checks
Ground Training					**Flight Training**		
				STAGE V			
	2.0			Ground Lesson 40			
				Flight Lesson 31	2.0		
				Flight Lesson 32	2.0		
	2.0			Ground Lesson 41			
				Flight Lesson 33	1.5		
				Flight Lesson 34	2.0		
	2.0			Ground Lesson 42			
				Flight Lesson 35	1.5		
	2.0			Ground Lesson 43			
				Flight Lesson 36	1.5		
		.5	As Req.	Ground Lesson 44 – Stage V Exam			
				Flight Lesson 37 – Stage Check	1.5		1.5
	8.0	.5	As Req.	Stage Totals	12.0		1.5
				STAGE VI			
				Flight Lesson 38		1.5	
	2.0			Ground Lesson 45			
				Flight Lesson 39		2.0	
	2.0			Ground Lesson 46			
				Flight Lesson 40		1.5	
				Flight Lesson 41		1.5	
	2.0			Ground Lesson 47			
				Flight Lesson 42		1.5	
2.0		1.0		Ground Lesson 48 – Briefing and Stage VI Exam			
				Flight Lesson 43		1.5	
		1.5	1.0	Ground Lesson 49 – End-of-Course Exam			
				Flight Lesson 44 – Stage Check		1.5	1.5
				Flight Lesson 45 – End-of-Course Check		2.0	2.0
2.0	6.0	2.5	1.0	Stage Totals		13.0	3.5
2.0	14.0	3.0	1.0	Course Totals	12.0	13.0	5.0

NOTE: *Individual times shown are for guidance only; they are not mandatory for each lesson. However, the totals in each category should be attained at the completion of each stage to ensure the student will acquire the minimum instruction required by Part 141. Preflight and postflight briefing times are as required.*

Multi-Engine Instructor Ground Training Syllabus

Stage V

Stage Objectives
During Stage V, the applicant will review the concepts and principles of multi-engine operations, systems, engine-out operations, and the aerodynamics of multi-engine flight. The applicant will also obtain the instructional knowledge required to teach these subjects including the recognition, analysis, and correction of common student errors.

Stage Completion Standards
This Stage is complete when the applicant has completed the Multi-Engine Flight Instructor Stage Exam with a minimum passing score of 80 percent and the instructor has reviewed each incorrect response to ensure complete understanding.

Stage V

Ground Lesson 40

Lesson References:

Flight Instructor Textbook

Chapter 6, Section C — Integrating Multi-Engine Knowledge

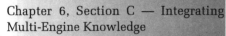

GFD Multi-Engine Video

Recommended Sequence:
1. Lesson Introduction and Video Presentation
2. Class Discussion

Lesson Objectives:
During this lesson, the applicant will review fundamentals of instruction knowledge areas and obtain instructional knowledge of multi-engine systems, engine-out aerodynamics, performance, and limitations, including V-speeds. In addition, the applicant will learn about multi-engine weight considerations, single-engine ceilings, and decision making in multi-engine training.

Content:

Lesson Review:

FUNDAMENTALS OF INSTRUCTION

- ❑ The Learning Process
- ❑ The Teaching Process
- ❑ Teaching Methods
- ❑ Evaluation
- ❑ Flight Instructor Characteristics and Responsibilities
- ❑ Human Factors
- ❑ Planning Instructional Activity

SECTION C — INTEGRATING MULTI-ENGINE KNOWLEDGE

- ❑ Instructing in Multi-Engine Airplanes
- ❑ Explaining Multi-Engine Systems
- ❑ Electrical Systems
- ❑ Fuel Systems
- ❑ Propellers
- ❑ Synchronization
- ❑ Feathering
- ❑ Unfeathering
- ❑ Teaching Engine-Out Aerodynamics
- ❑ Zero Sideslip
- ❑ Critical Engine
- ❑ Minimum Control Airspeed
- ❑ Centerline Thrust
- ❑ Interpreting Performance Considerations and Limitations
- ❑ Drag Reduction Following Engine Failure
- ❑ Pilot's Operating Handbook
- ❑ Airspeed Limitations
- ❑ Published V_{MC}

- ❑ V_Y
- ❑ V_{YSE}
- ❑ V_{XSE}
- ❑ V_{SSE}
- ❑ Accelerate-Stop Distance
- ❑ Accelerate-Go Distance
- ❑ Density Altitude Considerations
- ❑ Weight Limitations
- ❑ Zero Fuel Weight
- ❑ Single-Engine Ceilings
- ❑ Integrating Decision Making in Multi-Engine Training
- ❑ Accident Statistics
- ❑ Preflight and Takeoff Briefings
- ❑ Instrument-Rated Multi-Engine Applicants

COMPLETION STANDARDS:

Through oral quizzing, the instructor will determine that the applicant understands the FOI knowledge areas. In addition, the applicant will complete Chapter 6C questions with a minimum passing score of 80 percent, and the instructor will review each incorrect response to ensure complete understanding before the applicant progresses to Ground Lesson 41.

STUDY ASSIGNMENT:

FLIGHT INSTRUCTOR TEXTBOOK

Chapter 6, Section D — Mastering Multi-Engine Skills

STAGE V

GROUND LESSON 41

LESSON REFERENCES:

FLIGHT INSTRUCTOR TEXTBOOK

Chapter 6, Section D, Mastering Multi-Engine Skills

RECOMMENDED SEQUENCE:
1. Lesson Introduction
2. Class Discussion

LESSON OBJECTIVES:
During this lesson, the applicant will obtain instructional knowledge of multi-engine maneuvers and procedures. The applicant will review engine-out operations, including the aerodynamics associated with single-engine procedures and maneuvers. In addition, the applicant will gain an understanding of the importance of engine-out operations within the scope of a multi-engine training program.

CONTENT:

SECTION D — MASTERING MULTI-ENGINE SKILLS

AIRCRAFT FAMILIARIZATION
❑ Preflight
❑ Staring Engines
❑ Taxiing
❑ Takeoff Considerations
❑ Maximum Performance Takeoff
❑ Approach and Landing

TEACHING SAFE GO-AROUND PROCEDURES
❑ Teaching Multi-Engine Maneuvers
❑ Steep Turns
❑ Maneuvering During Slow Flight

❑ Stalls
❑ Emergency Operations
❑ Introduction to Engine-Out Maneuvering
❑ Simulated Engine-Out Maneuvering
❑ Engine-Out Procedures
❑ Engine-Out Maneuvers
❑ Simulated Engine-Out Takeoff
❑ Simulated Engine-Out Approaches and Landings
❑ V_{MC} Demonstration
❑ Drag Demonstration
❑ Importance of Zero Sideslip
❑ Safety Considerations for Engine-Out Training
❑ Spin Considerations
❑ Obtaining Multi-Engine Instrument Procedures

COMPLETION STANDARDS:
The applicant will complete Chapter 6D questions with a minimum passing score of 80 percent, and the instructor will review each incorrect response to ensure complete understanding before the applicant progresses to Ground Lesson 42.

STUDY ASSIGNMENT:
Review the training airplane's Pilot's Operating Handbook and FAA-Approved Airplane Flight Manual

---

STAGE V

GROUND LESSON 42

LESSON REFERENCES:
Pilot's Operating Handbook (POH) and FAA-Approved Airplane Flight Manual

RECOMMENDED SEQUENCE:
1. Lesson Introduction
2. Class Discussion

LESSON OBJECTIVES:
During this lesson, the applicant will obtain instructional knowledge of the information contained in the POH or Airplane Flight Manual for the training

airplane. Specifically, the applicant will learn to examine and understand important limitations, normal/emergency procedures, performance data, weight and balance computations, and systems, including basic handling, servicing, and maintenance procedures.

CONTENT:

LESSON REVIEW:

PILOT'S OPERATING HANDBOOK
❑ General
❑ Limitations
❑ Emergency procedures
❑ Abnormal Procedures (If Applicable)
❑ Normal Procedures
❑ Performance
❑ Weight and Balance Equipment List (If Applicable)

❑ Description of the Airplane and Its Systems
❑ Handling, Servicing, and Maintenance
❑ Supplements
❑ Safety and Operational Tips (If Applicable)

COMPLETION STANDARDS:
Through oral quizzing, the instructor will determine that the applicant understands the material covered in this lesson before progressing to Ground Lesson 43.

STUDY ASSIGNMENT:
Review the aeronautical knowledge areas required to teach as a Multi-Engine Flight Instructor.

STAGE V

GROUND LESSON 43

LESSON REFERENCES:

Parts 61, 141

Practical Test Standards (Private and Commercial Pilot Airplane Multi-Engine Land, Instrument Rating-Airplane)

Airplane Flying Handbook, FAA-H-8083-3

RECOMMENDED SEQUENCE:
1. Lesson Introduction
2. Class Discussion

LESSON OBJECTIVES:
During this lesson, the applicant will gain additional insight into the aeronautical knowledge requirements needed to teach students in multi-engine airplanes. Specifically, the applicant will review the applicable regulations, Practical Test Standards, and other pertinent aeronautical publications for the most up-to-date information on learning to fly multi-engine airplanes.

CONTENT:

REGULATIONS AND RELATED PUBLICATIONS
❑ FAR Part 61 (Subparts B, E, F)
❑ FAR Part 141 (Appendices B,C,D)
❑ Practical Test Standards (Private Pilot Airplane Multi-Engine Land, Commercial Pilot Airplane Multi-

Engine Land, Instrument Rating-Airplane)
- *Airplane Flying Handbook*, FAA-H-8083-3, (Applicable Chapters)
- Current FAA Advisory Circulars (Applicable Subjects)

COMMERCIAL PILOT AERONAUTICAL KNOWLEDGE AREAS

- Applicable Sections of Part 61 Related to Commercial Pilot Privileges, Limitations, and Flight Operations
- NTSB Accident Reporting Requirements
- Basic Aerodynamics and the Principles of Flight
- Meteorology to Include Recognition of Critical Weather Situations, Wind shear Recognition and Avoidance, and the Use of Aeronautical Weather Reports and Forecasts
- Safe and Efficient Operation of Aircraft
- Weight and Balance Computations
- Use of Performance Charts
- Significance and Effects of Exceeding Aircraft Performance Limitations

- Use of Aeronautical Charts and a Magnetic Compass for Pilotage and Dead Reckoning
- Use of Air Navigation Facilities
- Aeronautical Decision Making and Judgment
- Principles and Functions of Aircraft Systems
- Maneuvers, Procedures, and Emergency Operations Appropriate to the Aircraft
- Night and High-Altitude Operations
- Procedures for Operating within the National Airspace System

COMPLETION STANDARDS:
Through oral quizzing, the instructor will determine that the applicant understands the material covered in this lesson before progressing to Ground Lesson 44.

STUDY ASSIGNMENT:
Review the *Flight Instructor* textbook, Chapter 6, Sections C and D, the training airplane POH, applicable regulations, and related publications in preparation for the Stage V Exam.

STAGE V

GROUND LESSON 44

STAGE V EXAM

RECOMMENDED SEQUENCE:
1. Lesson Introduction
2. Testing
3. Critique

LESSON OBJECTIVES:
The exam administered during this lesson evaluates the applicant's comprehension of the material covered in Stage V.

CONTENT:
Multi-Engine Flight Instructor Stage V Exam

COMPLETION STANDARDS:
This lesson and stage are complete when the applicant has completed the

exam with a minimum passing score of 80 percent, and the instructor has reviewed each incorrect response to ensure complete understanding before progressing to Stage VI.

STUDY ASSIGNMENT:
Review multi-engine performance considerations.

STAGE VI

STAGE OBJECTIVES

During Stage VI, the applicant will review the principles and concepts of multi-engine performance, complex airplane systems, and environmental systems. In addition, the applicant will obtain the instructional knowledge required to teach these subjects.

STAGE COMPLETION STANDARD

This Stage is complete when the applicant has completed the Multi-Engine Flight Instructor End-of-Course Exam with a minimum passing score of 80 percent, and the instructor has reviewed each incorrect response to ensure complete understanding.

STAGE VI

GROUND LESSON 45

RECOMMENDED SEQUENCE:

1. Lesson Introduction
2. Class Discussion

LESSON OBJECTIVES:

During this lesson, the applicant will obtain the instructional knowledge required to teach the performance considerations associated with multi-engine airplanes.

CONTENT:

❏ Airplane Weight and Balance
❏ Performance Charts
❏ Performance Factors

COMPLETION STANDARDS:

Through oral quizzing, the instructor will determine that the applicant has obtained the instructional knowledge required to teach the performance considerations associated with multi-engine airplanes before progressing to Ground Lesson 46.

STUDY ASSIGNMENT:

Review advanced airplane systems.

STAGE VI

GROUND LESSON 46

RECOMMENDED SEQUENCE:

1. Lesson Introduction
2. Class Discussion

LESSON OBJECTIVES:

During this lesson, the applicant will obtain the instructional knowledge required to teach the principles and operations of complex airplanes systems typically found in multi-engine airplanes.

CONTENT:

❏ Controllable Pitch Propellers
❏ Fuel Injection and Turbocharging

❑ Landing Gear Systems
❑ Electrical System
❑ Hydraulic System
❑ Electro-Hydraulic System
❑ Circuit Breakers
❑ Airspeed Limitations
❑ Emergency Gear Extensions

COMPLETION STANDARDS:
Through oral quizzing, the instructor will determine that the applicant has obtained the instructional knowledge required to teach the principles and operations of complex airplane systems typically found in multi-engine airplanes before progressing to Ground Lesson 47.

STUDY ASSIGNMENT:
Review environmental systems.

STAGE VI

GROUND LESSON 47

RECOMMENDED SEQUENCE:
1. Lesson Introduction
2. Class Discussion

LESSON OBJECTIVES:
During this lesson, the applicant will obtain the instructional knowledge required to teach the principles and operations of environmental systems typically found in multi-engine airplanes.

CONTENT:
❑ Oxygen Systems
❑ Cabin Pressurization
❑ Ice Control Equipment and Systems

COMPLETION STANDARDS:
Through oral quizzing, the instructor will determine that the applicant has obtained the instructional knowledge required to teach the principles and operations of environmental systems typically found in multi-engine airplanes.

STUDY ASSIGNMENT:
Complete preparation for the Multi-Engine Flight Instructor Oral Questions Pilot Briefing.

STAGE VI

GROUND LESSON 48

PILOT BRIEFING AND STAGE VI EXAM

LESSON REFERENCE:

FLIGHT INSTRUCTOR TEXTBOOK

Chapter 6, Section C, Integrating Multi-Engine Knowledge, and Section D, Mastering Multi-Engine Flight Skills

RECOMMENDED SEQUENCE:
1. Lesson Introduction
2. Class Discussion
3. Testing
4. Critiquing

LESSON OBJECTIVES:
Prior to this lesson, the applicant will prepare answers to the essay questions contained in the Multi-Engine Flight Instructor Oral Questions Pilot Briefing using appropriate references. During the discussion, the applicant will explain the answers given and demonstrate that the material is thoroughly understood. In addition, the applicant will demonstrate the ability to apply this knowledge to multi-engine flight instruction. The exam administered during this lesson evaluates student comprehension of the material covered in Stage VI.

CONTENT:

MULTI-ENGINE FLIGHT INSTRUCTOR ORAL QUESTIONS
❑ Analysis of a Maneuver

❑ Multi-Engine Performance and Aerodynamics
❑ Engine-Out Performance and Aerodynamics
❑ Multi-Engine Emergency Procedures
❑ General Subjects
❑ Stage VI Exam

COMPLETION STANDARDS:
The applicant will demonstrate that each question is completely understood and the information can be clearly conveyed to a student. This lesson and stage are complete when the applicant has completed the Stage VI Exam with a minimum passing score of 80 percent, and the instructor has reviewed each incorrect response to ensure complete understanding before progressing to the End-of-Course Examination.

STUDY ASSIGNMENT:
The applicant should review the *Flight Instructor* textbook, as necessary, in preparation for the Multi-Engine Flight Instructor End-of-Course Examination.

STAGE VI

GROUND LESSON 49

MULTI-ENGINE FLIGHT INSTRUCTOR END-OF-COURSE EXAM

RECOMMENDED SEQUENCE:
1. Lesson Introduction
2. Testing
3. Critique

LESSON OBJECTIVES:
This testing session evaluates the applicant's comprehension of the material presented in Stages V and VI.

CONTENT:
Multi-Engine Flight Instructor Final Examination.

COMPLETION STANDARDS:
The applicant will complete the Multi-Engine Flight Instructor Final Exam with a minimum passing score of 80 percent, and the instructor will review each incorrect response to ensure complete understanding.

MULTI-ENGINE INSTRUCTOR FLIGHT TRAINING SYLLABUS
STAGE V

STAGE OBJECTIVES
During this stage, the applicant will learn the analysis and performance of the maneuvers and procedures from the right seat of the multi-engine training airplane. The maneuvers and procedures are those required for multi-engine land class rating certification.

STAGE COMPLETION STANDARDS
The applicant must successfully complete each of the lessons in Stage V. Additionally, the applicant will be able to analyze and perform all of the listed maneuvers and procedures from the right seat of the multi-engine training airplane in accordance with the criteria set forth in the multi-engine land sections of the current FAA private pilot, commercial pilot, and flight instructor practical test standards, as appropriate.

STAGE V

FLIGHT LESSON 31

DUAL

LESSON OBJECTIVES:
During this lesson, the applicant will learn the fundamentals of analyzing and performing basic multi-engine operations and become familiar with the visual perspective and control usage when flying from the right seat of the training airplane. The applicant will discuss how the use of checklists is an essential element of effective resource use and workload management.

CONTENT:

LESSON INTRODUCTION

PREFLIGHT PREPARATION
❑ Certificates and Documents
❑ Airworthiness Requirements
❑ Weather Information
❑ National Airspace System
❑ Aeromedical Factors

MULTI-ENGINE OPERATIONS
❑ Operation of Systems
❑ Performance and Limitations
❑ Flight Principles — Engine Inoperative
❑ Emergency Procedures
❑ Aeronautical Decision Making and Judgment

PREFLIGHT PROCEDURES
❑ Use of Checklists
❑ Preflight Inspection
❑ Single-Pilot Resource Management
❑ Engine Starting
❑ Taxiing, Normal, Crosswind, Differential Power

- ❑ Positive Exchange of Controls
- ❑ Before Takeoff Check

AIRPORT OPERATIONS
- ❑ Radio Communications and ATC Light Signals
- ❑ Airport, Runway, and Taxiway Signs, Markings, and Lighting
- ❑ Runway Incursion Avoidance
  - ❑ Use of aircraft lighting during taxi and takeoff operations.
  - ❑ Readback/hearback on
    (1) Hold Short,
    (2) Position and Hold, and
    (3) Runway Crossings.
- ❑ Land and Hold Short Operations (LAHSO)

TAKEOFFS AND CLIMBS
- ❑ Normal
- ❑ Crosswind

TRAFFIC PATTERNS

VISUAL SCANNING AND COLLISION AVOIDANCE

STRAIGHT-AND-LEVEL FLIGHT

CHANGES OF AIRSPEED/ALTITUDE

TURNS
- ❑ Level
- ❑ Steep

CLIMBS
- ❑ Straight
- ❑ Turning

DESCENTS
- ❑ Straight
- ❑ Turning

APPROACHES AND LANDINGS
- ❑ Normal
- ❑ Crosswind

POSTFLIGHT PROCEDURES
- ❑ After Landing
- ❑ Parking and Securing

COMPLETION STANDARDS:
At the completion of this lesson, the applicant will be able to analyze and perform the proper procedures for multi-engine operations, ground operations, and basic multi-engine procedures as outlined in the lesson. During all operations, the applicant will maintain a constant vigilance and awareness of all other traffic.

POSTFLIGHT DISCUSSION AND PREVIEW OF NEXT LESSON

STAGE V

FLIGHT LESSON 32

DUAL

LESSON OBJECTIVES:
During this lesson, the applicant will demonstrate the accurate analysis and develop the ability to perform the maneuvers and procedures listed for

review. In addition, the applicant will begin to learn the analysis and performance of maneuvering during slow flight. The applicant will explain the importance of maintaining situational awareness to prevent runway incursion incidents.

CONTENT:

LESSON REVIEW

MULTI-ENGINE OPERATIONS
- ❑ Operation of Systems
- ❑ Performance and Limitations
- ❑ Flight Principles — Engine Inoperative
- ❑ Airworthiness Requirements
- ❑ Engine Inoperative
- ❑ Taxiing, Normal, Crosswind, Differential Power
- ❑ Positive Exchange of Controls
- ❑ Before Takeoff Check

AIRPORT OPERATIONS
- ❑ Radio Communication and ATC Light Signals
- ❑ Airport, Runway, and Taxiway Signs, Markings, and Lighting
- ❑ Runway Incursion Avoidance/ LAHSO

TAKEOFFS AND CLIMBS
- ❑ Normal
- ❑ Crosswind

TRAFFIC PATTERNS

VISUAL SCANNING AND COLLISION AVOIDANCE

STRAIGHT-AND-LEVEL FLIGHT

CHANGES OF AIRSPEED/ALTITUDE

TURNS
- ❑ Level
- ❑ Steep

CLIMBS
- ❑ Straight
- ❑ Turning

DESCENTS
- ❑ Straight
- ❑ Turning

APPROACHES AND LANDINGS
- ❑ Normal
- ❑ Crosswind

POSTFLIGHT PROCEDURES

LESSON INTRODUCTION

GROUND REFERENCE MANEUVERS
- ❑ Rectangular Course
- ❑ S-Turns
- ❑ Turns Around a Point

SLOW FLIGHT AND STALLS
- ❑ Power-On Stalls
- ❑ Power-Off Stalls
- ❑ Maneuvering During Slow Flight
- ❑ Accelerated Maneuver Stalls (Demonstration)   ←
- ❑ Spin Awareness

COMPLETION STANDARDS:
At the completion of this lesson, the applicant will be able to perform ground references maneuvers and maneuvering during slow flight. This will include the explanation of how each element is important to the performance of the entire maneuver or procedure. In addition, the applicant will be able to demonstrate the correct analysis and performance of the maneuvers and procedures listed for review.

POSTFLIGHT DISCUSSION AND PREVIEW OF NEXT LESSON

LESSON ASSIGNMENT:
Ground Lesson 41

STAGE V

FLIGHT LESSON 33

DUAL

LESSON OBJECTIVES:

During this lesson, the applicant will develop the ability to demonstrate the accurate analysis and performance of the maneuvers and procedures listed for review. In addition, the applicant will learn the analysis and performance of short-field takeoffs, approaches and landings, and go-arounds. The applicant will discuss how aeronautical decision making (ADM) principles apply to exercising good judgment when executing takeoffs, landings, and go-arounds.

CONTENT:

LESSON REVIEW

❑ Multi-Engine Operations
❑ Preflight Procedures

SLOW FLIGHT AND STALLS

❑ Power-On Stalls
❑ Power-Off Stalls
❑ Maneuvering During Slow Flight

❑ Accelerated Maneuver Stalls
  (Demonstration)
❑ Spin Awareness

GROUND REFERENCE MANEUVERS

❑ Rectangular Course
❑ S-Turns
❑ Turns Around a Point

LESSON INTRODUCTION

❑ Short-field Takeoff and Maximum
  Performance Climb
❑ Short-Field Approach and Landing
❑ Go-Around/Rejected Landing

COMPLETION STANDARDS:

At the completion of this lesson, the applicant will be able to analyze and perform multi-engine operations, ground operations, stalls, and maneuvering during slow flight. In addition, the applicant will be able to demonstrate the correct procedure for short-field takeoffs, approaches and landings, and go-arounds. This will include the explanation of how each element is important to the performance of the entire maneuver or procedure demonstrated.

POSTFLIGHT DISCUSSION AND PREVIEW OF NEXT LESSON

STAGE V

FLIGHT LESSON 34

DUAL

LESSON OBJECTIVES:

During this lesson, the applicant will develop the ability to demonstrate the accurate analysis and performance of the maneuvers and procedures listed for review. The applicant will learn the analysis and performance of the listed emergency procedures. In addition, the applicant will discuss ADM principles, such as workload management, which apply when transitioning to complex multi-engine airplanes.

CONTENT:

LESSON REVIEW

❑ Short-Field Takeoff and Maximum
  Performance Climb

❑ Short-Field Approach and Landing
❑ Go-Around/Rejected Landing

LESSON INTRODUCTION

EMERGENCY OPERATIONS/PROCEDURES
❑ Emergency Descent
❑ Systems and Equipment Malfunctions
❑ Identification of Inoperative Engine
❑ Maneuvering with One Engine Inoperative
❑ V_{MC} Demonstration
❑ Demonstrating the Effect of Various Airspeeds and Configurations During Engine Inoperative Performance

COMPLETION STANDARDS:
At the completion of this lesson, the applicant will be able to analyze and perform maximum approaches and landings and go-arounds. In addition, the applicant will be able to demonstrate the correct performance of the listed emergency operations. This will include the explanation of how each element is important to the performance of the entire maneuver or procedure.

POSTFLIGHT DISCUSSION AND PREVIEW OF NEXT LESSON

LESSON ASSIGNMENT:
Ground Lesson 42

STAGE V

FLIGHT LESSON 35

DUAL

LESSON OBJECTIVES:
During this lesson, the applicant will develop the ability to demonstrate the accurate analysis and performance of the emergency operations listed for review. The applicant also will learn the analysis and performance of the emergency operations introduced. In addition, the applicant will demonstrate the ability to identify and discuss operational pitfalls which apply to engine-out operations and procedures.

CONTENT:

LESSON REVIEW

EMERGENCY OPERATIONS/PROCEDURES
❑ Emergency Descent
❑ Systems and Equipment Malfunctions
❑ Identification of Inoperative Engine
❑ Maneuvering with One Engine Inoperative
❑ V_{MC} Demonstration
❑ Demonstrating the Effects of Various Airspeeds and Configurations During Engine Inoperative Performance

LESSON INTRODUCTION

EMERGENCY OPERATIONS/PROCEDURES

- Engine Failure During Takeoff Before V_{MC} (Simulated)
- Engine Failure After Lift-Off (Simulated)
- Emergency Equipment and Survival Gear
- Approach and Landing with an Engine Inoperative (Simulated)

COMPLETION STANDARDS:

At the completion of this lesson, the applicant will be able to analyze and perform the emergency operations listed for review. In addition, the applicant will be able to demonstrate the correct performance of the emergency operations listed for introduction. This will include the explanation of how each element is important to the performance of the entire maneuver or procedure.

POSTFLIGHT DISCUSSION AND PREVIEW OF NEXT LESSON

LESSON ASSIGNMENT:

Ground Lesson 43

STAGE V

FLIGHT LESSON 36

DUAL

LESSON OBJECTIVES:

During this lesson, the applicant will develop the ability to demonstrate the accurate analysis and performance of the listed emergency operations. In addition, the applicant will apply relevant ADM principles to emergency operations and procedures, including workload management, communication, and resource use.

CONTENT:

LESSON REVIEW

EMERGENCY OPERATIONS/PROCEDURES

- V_{MC} Demonstration
- Engine Failure During Takeoff Before V_{MC} (Simulated)
- Engine Failure After Lift-Off (Simulated)
- Emergency Equipment and Survival Gear
- Approach and Landing with an Engine Inoperative (Simulated)
- Aeronautical Decision Making and Judgment

LESSON INTRODUCTION

BASIC INSTRUMENT MANEUVERS, FULL AND PARTIAL PANEL

- Turns
- Steep Turns
- Timed Turns to Magnetic Compass Headings
- Change of Airspeed
- Constant Airspeed Climbs and Descents
- Constant Rate Climbs and Descents
- Recovery from Unusual Flight Attitudes

COMPLETION STANDARDS: At the completion of this lesson, the applicant will be able to demonstrate the correct analysis and performance of each of the listed emergency operations. This will include the explanation of how each element is important to the performance of the entire maneuver or procedure.

POSTFLIGHT DISCUSSION AND PREVIEW OF NEXT LESSON

LESSON ASSIGNMENT: Ground Lesson 44

STAGE V

FLIGHT LESSON 37

DUAL — STAGE CHECK

LESSON OBJECTIVES:
This lesson is a stage check, conducted by the chief instructor or the designated assistant, to evaluate the applicant's ability to correctly analyze and perform the listed maneuvers and procedures. In addition, the applicant's ability to apply the ADM principles of pilot-in-command responsibility, communication, workload management, resource use and situational awareness to ground and flight operations will be evaluated.

CONTENT:

LESSON REVIEW
❑ Multi-Engine Operations
❑ Preflight Procedures
❑ Takeoffs and Climbs
❑ Airport Operations
❑ Traffic Patterns
❑ Visual Scanning and Collision Avoidance
❑ Straight-and-Level Flight
❑ Turns
❑ Climbs
❑ Descents
❑ Ground Reference Maneuvers
❑ Approaches and Landings
❑ Ground Reference Maneuvers
❑ Slow Flight and Stalls
❑ Emergency Operations/Procedures
❑ Postflight Procedures

COMPLETION STANDARDS:
At the completion of this lesson, the applicant will be able to demonstrate the performance of each of the listed maneuvers and procedures at a proficiency level which meets or exceeds those criteria outlined in the multi-engine land sections of the current FAA private pilot, commercial pilot, and flight instructor practical test standards, as appropriate. In addition, the applicant will be able to correctly analyze the elements associated with the performance of each maneuver and procedure. Finally, the applicant will exhibit sound ADM and judgment skills.

POSTFLIGHT DISCUSSION AND PREVIEW OF NEXT LESSON

STAGE VI

STAGE OBJECTIVES

During this stage, the applicant will acquire the instructional knowledge of the elements of each of the listed maneuvers and procedures including the recognition, analysis, and correction of common student errors. The applicant will be able to prepare a lesson plan for each flight in Stage VI and conduct the flight according to the planned lesson, including effective preflight and postflight instruction.

STAGE COMPLETION STANDARDS

The applicant will successfully complete each of the Flight Lessons in Stage VI. At the completion of the stage, the applicant will have the proficiency and instructional knowledge of a competent multi-engine flight instructor. The proficiency level will meet or exceed the criteria outlined in the multi-engine land sections of the private pilot, commercial pilot and flight instructor practical test standards, as appropriate.

STAGE VI

FLIGHT LESSON 38

DUAL

LESSON OBJECTIVES:

During this lesson, the applicant will obtain the instructional knowledge of the elements of basic multi-engine operations. This will include the recognition, analysis, and correction of common student errors. The applicant also will demonstrate the ability to incorporate ADM principles into flight lessons. For example, the use of checklists can be emphasized as an important resource used to enhance a student's ability to manage workload.

CONTENT:

LESSON INTRODUCTION

PREFLIGHT PREPARATION
- ❏ Certificates and Documents
- ❏ Weather Information
- ❏ National Airspace Systems
- ❏ Aeromedical Factors

MULTI-ENGINE OPERATIONS
- ❏ Operation of Systems
- ❏ Performance and Limitations
- ❏ Flight Principles — Engine Inoperative
- ❏ Airworthiness Requirements
- ❏ Emergency Procedures

PREFLIGHT PROCEDURES
- ❏ Use of Checklists
- ❏ Preflight Inspection
- ❏ Single-Pilot Resource Management
- ❏ Engine Starting
- ❏ Taxiing, Normal, Crosswind, Differential Power
- ❏ Positive Exchange of Controls
- ❏ Before Takeoff Check

AIRPORT OPERATIONS
❑ Radio Communications and ATC Light Signals
❑ Airport, Runway, and Taxiway Signs, Markings, and Lighting
❑ Runway Incursion Avoidance
  ❑ Use of aircraft lighting during taxi and takeoff operations.
  ❑ Readback/hearback on
    (1) Hold Short,
    (2) Position and Hold, and
    (3) Runway Crossings.
❑ Land and Hold Short Operations (LAHSO)

TAKEOFFS AND CLIMBS
❑ Normal
❑ Crosswind

TRAFFIC PATTERNS

VISUAL SCANNING AND COLLISION AVOIDANCE

STRAIGHT-AND-LEVEL FLIGHT

CHANGES OF AIRSPEED/ALTITUDE

TURNS
❑ Level
❑ Steep

CLIMBS
❑ Straight
❑ Turning

DESCENTS
❑ Straight
❑ Turning

APPROACHES AND LANDINGS
❑ Normal
❑ Crosswind

POSTFLIGHT PROCEDURES
❑ After Landing
❑ Parking and Securing

COMPLETION STANDARDS:
At the completion of this lesson, the applicant will be able to perform each of the maneuvers and procedures at the competency level that meets or exceeds the criteria outlined in the multi-engine land sections of the current FAA private pilot, commercial pilot, and flight instructor practical test standards, as appropriate. In addition, the applicant will demonstrate the instructional knowledge of the elements of the maneuver or procedure and the common errors, including recognition, analysis, and correction.

POSTFLIGHT DISCUSSION AND PREVIEW OF NEXT LESSON

LESSON ASSIGNMENT:
Ground Lesson 45

STAGE VI

FLIGHT LESSON 39

DUAL

LESSON OBJECTIVES:
During this lesson, the applicant will practice the review maneuvers and procedures to further develop instructional techniques. In addition, the applicant will obtain the instructional knowledge of the elements of ground reference maneuvers, maneuvering during slow flight, and stalls, including the recognition, analysis, and correction of common student errors. The applicant will demonstrate the ability to present ADM concepts to students, such as the importance of maintaining situational awareness to prevent runway incursion incidents.

CONTENT:

LESSON REVIEW

MULTI-ENGINE OPERATIONS
❑ Airplane Systems
❑ Performance and Limitations
❑ Flight Principles — Engine Inoperative
❑ Airworthiness Requirements
❑ Emergency Procedures

PREFLIGHT PROCEDURES
❑ Preflight Inspection
❑ Single-Pilot Resource Management
❑ Engine Starting
❑ Taxiing, Normal, Crosswind, Differential Power
❑ Positive Exchange of Controls
❑ Before Takeoff Check

AIRPORT OPERATIONS
❑ Radio Communications and ATC Light Signals
❑ Airport, Runway, and Taxiway Signs, Markings, and Lighting
❑ Runway Incursion Avoidance

TAKEOFFS AND CLIMBS
❑ Normal
❑ Crosswind

TRAFFIC PATTERNS

VISUAL SCANNING AND COLLISION AVOIDANCE

STRAIGHT-AND-LEVEL FLIGHT

CHANGES OF AIRSPEED/ALTITUDE

TURNS
❑ Level
❑ Steep

CLIMBS
❑ Straight
❑ Turning

DESCENTS
❑ Straight
❑ Turning

APPROACHES AND LANDINGS
❑ Normal
❑ Crosswind

POSTFLIGHT PROCEDURES

LESSON INTRODUCTION

GROUND REFERENCE MANEUVERS
❑ Rectangular Course
❑ S-Turns
❑ Turns Around a Point

SLOW FLIGHT AND STALLS
❑ Maneuvering During Slow Flight
❑ Power-On Stalls
❑ Power-Off Stalls
❑ Accelerated Maneuver Stalls (Demonstration) ◄
❑ Spin Awareness

COMPLETION STANDARDS:
At the completion of this lesson, the applicant will be able to analyze and perform each of the listed maneuvers and procedures at a proficiency level that meets or exceeds the criteria outlined in the multi-engine land sections of the current FAA private pilot, commercial pilot, and flight instructor practical test standards, as appropriate. In addition, the applicant will demonstrate the instructional knowledge of the elements of the maneuvers and procedures listed for review, including the recognition, analysis, and correction of common student errors.

POSTFLIGHT DISCUSSION AND PREVIEW OF NEXT LESSON

LESSON ASSIGNMENT:
Ground Lesson 46

STAGE VI

FLIGHT LESSON 40

DUAL

LESSON OBJECTIVES:
During this lesson, the applicant will practice the review maneuvers and procedures to further develop instructional techniques. In addition, the applicant will obtain the instructional knowledge of the elements of short-field takeoffs and maximum performance climbs, approaches and landings, and go-arounds, including recognition, analysis, and correction of common student errors. The applicant will demonstrate how the practice of ADM principles can be included in lessons covering takeoffs, landings, and go-arounds.

CONTENT:

LESSON REVIEW

MULTI-ENGINE OPERATIONS

PREFLIGHT PROCEDURES

GROUND REFERENCE MANEUVERS
❑ Rectangular Course
❑ S-Turns
❑ Turns Around a Point

SLOW FLIGHT AND STALLS
❑ Power-On Stalls
❑ Power-Off Stalls
❑ Maneuvering During Slow Flight
❑ Accelerated Maneuver Stalls ⟵
  (Demonstration)
❑ Spin Awareness

LESSON INTRODUCTION

SHORT-FIELD TAKEOFF AND MAXIMUM PERFORMANCE CLIMB

SHORT-FIELD APPROACH AND LANDING

GO-AROUND/REJECTED LANDING

COMPLETION STANDARDS:
At the completion of this lesson, the applicant will be able to analyze and perform each of the listed maneuvers and procedures at a competency level that meets or exceeds the criteria outlined in the multi-engine land sections of the current FAA private pilot, commercial pilot, and flight instructor practical test standards, as appropriate. In addition, the applicant will demonstrate the instructional knowledge of the elements of the maneuvers and procedures listed for review, including recognition, analysis, and correction of the common errors.

STAGE VI

FLIGHT LESSON 41

DUAL

LESSON OBJECTIVES:
During this lesson, the applicant will practice the review maneuvers and procedures to further develop instructional techniques. The applicant will obtain the instructional knowledge of the elements of the listed emergency operations, including the recognition, analysis, and correction of common student errors. In addition, the applicant will demonstrate methods to incorporate a discussion of operational pitfalls during engine-out operations and procedures.

CONTENT:

LESSON REVIEW

SHORT-FIELD TAKEOFF AND MAXIMUM PERFORMANCE CLIMB

SHORT-FIELD APPROACH AND LANDING

GO-AROUND/REJECTED LANDING

LESSON INTRODUCTION

EMERGENCY OPERATIONS/PROCEDURES
- ❑ Emergency Descent
- ❑ Systems and Equipment Malfunctions
- ❑ Identification of Inoperative Engine
- ❑ Maneuvering with One Engine Inoperative
- ❑ V_{MC} Demonstration
- ❑ Demonstrating the Effect of Various Airspeeds and Configurations During Engine Inoperative Performance

COMPLETION STANDARDS:
At the completion of this lesson, the applicant will be able to analyze and perform each of the listed maneuvers and procedures at a competency level that meets or exceeds the criteria outlined in the multi- engine land sections of the private pilot, commercial pilot, and flight instructor practical test standards, as appropriate. The applicant will demonstrate the instructional knowledge of the elements of the maneuvers and procedures listed for review, including the recognition, analysis, and correction of common student errors.

POSTFLIGHT DISCUSSION AND PREVIEW OF NEXT LESSON

LESSON ASSIGNMENT:
Ground Lesson 47

STAGE VI

FLIGHT LESSON 42

DUAL

LESSON OBJECTIVES:
During this lesson, the applicant will practice the review maneuvers and procedures to further develop instructional techniques. The applicant will obtain the instructional knowledge of the elements of emergency operations listed for introduction, including recognition, analysis, and correction of common student errors. The applicant also will demonstrate methods to incorporate

ADM concepts, including workload management, communication, and resource use into lessons involving emergency operations and procedures.

CONTENT:

LESSON REVIEW

EMERGENCY OPERATIONS/PROCEDURES
- ❑ Emergency Descent
- ❑ Systems and Equipment Malfunctions
- ❑ Identification of Inoperative Engine
- ❑ Maneuvering with One Engine Inoperative
- ❑ V_{MC} Demonstration
- ❑ Demonstrating the Effects of Various Airspeeds and Configurations

During Engine Inoperative Performance

LESSON INTRODUCTION

EMERGENCY OPERATIONS/PROCEDURES
- ❑ Engine Failure During Takeoff Before V_{MC} (Simulated)
- ❑ Engine Failure After Lift-Off (Simulated)
- ❑ Approach and Landing with an Engine Inoperative (Simulated)
- ❑ Emergency Equipment and Survival Gear

COMPLETION STANDARDS:
At the completion of this lesson, the applicant will be able to analyze and perform each of the listed maneuvers and procedures at a competency level that meets or exceeds the criteria out-lined in the multi-engine land sections of the current FAA private pilot, commercial pilot, and flight instructor practical test standards, as appropriate. The applicant will demonstrate the instructional knowledge of the elements of the maneuvers and procedures, including recognition, analysis, and correction of common student errors.

POSTFLIGHT DISCUSSION AND PREVIEW OF NEXT LESSON

LESSON ASSIGNMENT:
Ground Lesson 48

STAGE VI

FLIGHT LESSON 43

DUAL

LESSON OBJECTIVES:
During this lesson, the applicant will practice the review maneuvers and procedures to further develop instructional techniques. The applicant will obtain the instructional knowledge of the elements of the listed emergency operations, including recognition, analysis, and correction of common student errors. The applicant will address how distractions can lead to a lack of situational awareness, resulting in loss of control during engine-out operations and procedures.

CONTENT:

LESSON REVIEW

EMERGENCY OPERATIONS/PROCEDURES
- ❑ V_{MC} Demonstration
- ❑ Engine Failure During Takeoff Before V_{MC} (Simulated)
- ❑ Engine Failure After Lift-Off (Simulated)
- ❑ Emergency Descent
- ❑ Approach and Landing with an Engine Inoperative (Simulated)
- ❑ Emergency Equipment and Survival Gear

COMPLETION STANDARDS:
At the completion of this lesson, the applicant will be able to analyze and perform each of the maneuvers and procedures at a proficiency level that

meets or exceeds the criteria outlined in the multi-engine land sections of the private pilot, commercial pilot, and flight instructor practical test standards, as appropriate. In addition, the applicant will demonstrate the instructional knowledge of the elements of the maneuvers and procedures, including recognition, analysis, and correction of common student errors.

POSTFLIGHT DISCUSSION AND PREVIEW OF NEXT LESSON

LESSON ASSIGNMENT:
Ground Lesson 49

STAGE VI

FLIGHT LESSON 44

DUAL — STAGE CHECK

LESSON OBJECTIVES:
During this lesson, the chief instructor, the assistant chief instructor, or a designated check instructor will determine that the applicant meets the proficiency requirements for a flight instructor certificate with an airplane, multi-engine land class rating. In addition, the applicant will demonstrate methods to incorporate the ADM principles of pilot-in-command responsibility, communication, workload management, resource use, and situational awareness to ground and flight operations.

CONTENT:

LESSON INTRODUCTION

MULTI-ENGINE OPERATIONS

PREFLIGHT LESSON ON MANEUVER TO BE PERFORMED IN FLIGHT

❑ Maneuver Lesson
❑ Preflight Procedures
❑ Airport Operations
❑ Takeoffs and Climbs
❑ Traffic Patterns
❑ Visual Scanning and Collision Avoidance
❑ Straight-and-Level Flight
❑ Turns
❑ Climbs
❑ Descents
❑ Approaches and Landings
❑ Ground Reference Maneuvers
❑ Slow Flight and Stalls
❑ Emergency Operations/Procedures
❑ Postflight Procedures

COMPLETION STANDARDS:
At the completion of this lesson, the applicant will demonstrate the skill and instructional knowledge required to successfully complete the flight instructor airplane, multi-engine practical test. Each maneuver and procedure will be performed at a proficiency level that meets or exceeds the criteria outlined in the multi-engine land sections of the current FAA private pilot, commercial pilot, and flight instructor practical test standards, as appropriate.

STAGE VI

FLIGHT LESSON 45

DUAL — END-OF-COURSE FLIGHT CHECK

LESSON OBJECTIVE

During this lesson, the chief instructor, assistant chief instructor, or a designated check instructor will determine that the applicant meets the knowledge and proficiency requirements for a flight instructor certificate with an airplane, single-engine class rating.

NOTE: *End-of-course flight checks include a broad range of knowledge and skill areas listed in the Flight Instructor Practical Test Standards (PTS). However, since it is impractical to complete all of the listed tasks on one flight check, the end-of-course checks should be conducted as a practical test. According to the practical test concept, an examiner may select specific tasks within an area of operation for testing purposes. Some areas of operation contain tasks that require the applicant to demonstrate instructional knowledge, others specify proficiency or demonstration of skill, and in some cases, certain tasks must be evaluated. All instructors and instructor applicants should be familiar with the practical test concept.*

CONTENT:

LESSON REVIEW

FUNDAMENTALS OF INSTRUCTING

- ❏ The Learning Process
- ❏ Human Behavior and Effective Communication
- ❏ The Teaching Process
- ❏ Teaching Methods
- ❏ Critique and Evaluation
- ❏ Flight Instructor Characteristics and Responsibilities
- ❏ Planning Instructional Activity

TECHNICAL SUBJECT AREAS

- ❏ Aeromedical Factors
- ❏ Visual Scanning and Collision Avoidance
- ❏ Principles of Flight
- ❏ Airplane Flight Controls
- ❏ Airplane Weight and Balance
- ❏ Navigation and Flight Planning
- ❏ Night Operations
- ❏ High Altitude Operations
- ❏ FARs and Publications
- ❏ National Airspace System
- ❏ Navigation Aids and Radar Services
- ❏ Logbook Entries and Certificate Endorsements

PREFLIGHT PREPARATION

- ❏ Certificates and Documents
- ❏ Weather Information
- ❏ Airworthiness Requirements

GROUND OPERATIONS

- ❏ Preflight Inspection
- ❏ Single-Pilot Resource Management ❑
- ❏ Engine Starting
- ❏ Taxiing
- ❏ Before Takeoff Check

AIRPORT OPERATIONS

- ❏ Radio Communications and ATC Light Signals
- ❏ Traffic Patterns
- ❏ Airport, Runway, and Taxiway Signs, Markings, and Lighting
- ❏ Runway Incursion Avoidance/ LAHSO

TAKEOFFS, LANDINGS AND GO-AROUNDS

- ❏ Normal and Crosswind Takeoff and Climb
- ❏ Short-Field Takeoff and Maximum Performance Climb
- ❏ Normal and Crosswind Approach and Landing

❏ Go-Around/Rejected Landing
❏ Short-Field Approach and Landing

FUNDAMENTALS OF FLIGHT
❏ Straight-and-Level Flight
❏ Level Turns
❏ Straight Climbs and Climbing Turns
❏ Straight Descents and Descending Turns

SLOW FLIGHT AND STALLS
❏ Maneuvering During Slow Flight
❏ Power-On Stalls (Proficiency)
❏ Power-Off Stalls (Proficiency)
→ ❏ Accelerated Maneuver Stalls (Demonstration)

BASIC INSTRUMENT MANEUVERS
❏ Straight-and-Level Flight
❏ Straight, Constant Airspeed Climbs
❏ Straight, Constant Airspeed Descents
❏ Turns to Headings
❏ Recovery from Unusual Flight Attitudes
❏ Navigation Aids and Radar Services

PERFORMANCE MANEUVERS
❏ Steep Turns

GROUND REFERENCE MANEUVERS
❏ Rectangular Course
❏ S-Turns
❏ Turns Around a Point

EMERGENCY OPERATIONS
❏ Systems and Equipment Malfunctions
❏ Engine Failure During Takeoff Before V_{MC} (Simulated)
❏ Engine Failure After Lift-Off (Simulated)
❏ Approach and Landing with an Inoperative Engine (Simulated)
❏ Emergency Descent

❏ Emergency Equipment and Survival Gear

INSTRUMENT FLIGHT — MULTI-ENGINE AIRCRAFT
❏ Engine Failure During Straight-and-Level Flight and Turns
❏ Instrument Approach – One Engine Inoperative

MULTI-ENGINE OPERATIONS
❏ Airplane Systems
❏ Performance and Limitations
❏ Flight Principles – Engine Inoperative
❏ Maneuvering with One Engine Inoperative
❏ V_{MC} Demonstration
❏ Demonstrating the Effects of Various Airspeeds and Configurations During Engine Inoperative Performance

PREFLIGHT LESSON ON A MANEUVER TO BE PERFORMED IN FLIGHT
❏ Maneuver Lesson

POSTFLIGHT PROCEDURES

COMPLETION STANDARDS:
At the completion of this lesson, the applicant will demonstrate satisfactory performance according to the appropriate FAA practical test standards with regard to:

1. knowledge of the fundamentals of instructing;
2. knowledge of the technical subject areas;
3. knowledge of the flight instructor's responsibilities concerning the pilot certification process;
4. knowledge of the flight instructor's responsibilities concerning logbook entries and pilot certificate endorsements;

5. ability to demonstrate the procedures and maneuvers selected by the examiner to at least the commercial pilot skill level while giving effective instruction;
6. competence in teaching the procedures and maneuvers selected by the examiner;
7. competence in describing, recognizing, analyzing, and correcting common errors simulated by the examiner; and
8. knowledge of the development and effective use of a course of training, a syllabus, and a lesson plan.

POSTFLIGHT DISCUSSION

This is to certify that

_____

is enrolled in the
Federal Aviation Administration
approved _____ **course**
conducted by_____.

_____   _____
Date of Enrollment   **Chief Instructor**

This is to certify that

_____

has successfully completed all stages, tests, and
course requirements and has graduated from the

FEDERAL AVIATION ADMINISTRATION

approved _____ **course**

conducted by _____.

The graduate has completed the training
specified in Part 141.

I certify the above statements are true.

☐ Flight Instructor Certification Course
(Airplane Single-Engine) —
Appendix F

☐ Flight Instructor Instrument Certification
Course (Airplane) —
Appendix G

☐ Flight Instructor Certification Course
(Airplane Multi-Engine)—
Appendix F

☐ Other: _____

_____

_____
Chief Instructor

_____
School certificate number

_____
Date of graduation

This is to certify that

_____

**is enrolled in the
Federal Aviation Administration
approved** _____ **course
conducted by**_____.

_____   _____
Date of Enrollment   **Chief Instructor**

This is to certify that

_____

**has successfully completed all stages, tests, and
course requirements and has graduated from the**

FEDERAL AVIATION ADMINISTRATION

approved _____ **course**

conducted by _____.

The graduate has completed the training
specified in Part 141.

I certify the above statements are true.

☐ Flight Instructor Certification Course
    (Airplane Single-Engine) —
        Appendix F
☐ Flight Instructor Instrument Certification
    Course (Airplane) —
        Appendix G
☐ Flight Instructor Certification Course
    (Airplane Multi-Engine)—
        Appendix F
☐ Other: _____
    _____

_____
Chief Instructor

_____
School certificate number

_____
Date of graduation

≈ This is to certify that ≈

_____

is enrolled in the
Federal Aviation Administration

approved _____ **course**

conducted by _____ .

_____   _____

Date of Enrollment   **Chief Instructor**

This is to certify that

_____

has successfully completed all stages, tests, and
course requirements and has graduated from the

FEDERAL AVIATION ADMINISTRATION

approved _____ **course**

conducted by _____ .

The graduate has completed the training
specified in Part 141.

☐ Flight Instructor Certification Course
   (Airplane Single-Engine) —
      Appendix F
☐ Flight Instructor Instrument Certification
   Course (Airplane) —
      Appendix G
☐ Flight Instructor Certification Course
   (Airplane Multi-Engine)—
      Appendix F
☐ Other: _____

_____

I certify the above statements are true.

_____
Chief Instructor

_____
School certificate number

_____
Date of graduation